"This is the book we need in the eating d
being transparent, relatable, acknow
expertise with specific and cool activities and tools to push us in healing our
relationships with food. I smiled reading this knowing so many will relate to
Colleen and Jennifer's personal stories and find healing through their lived
experience and easy to understand activities for recovery. This is how we
change the mental health game, through owning our stories and talking about
recovery in normalized and relatable ways. I'd recommend this book to every
single person I know living in diet culture (psst all of us)."

Tiffany Roe, MA, CMHC, Founder & CEO Mindful Counseling

"A book like this has the potential to make a massive difference. It's down-to-
earth, speaks to the actual needs and interests of the target audience, is written
by two highly-regarded leaders in the field, and may truly change and save lives.
This is a vital book, and I will personally refer my patients to buy it."

Jennifer Gaudiani, MD, founder and medical director
of Gaudiani Clinic, Author of *Sick Enough*

"Written with a breezy personal style, yet rooted in professional expertise and
research, *The Inside Scoop* is heartfelt, practical, and easy to read. If you ever
wanted to ask an eating disorder professional who had their own recovery
experience, 'Knowing what you know now, what do you wish you had known
while in the midst of your struggle?' – this book's for you."

Anita Johnston, PhD, Author of *Eating in the Light of the Moon*

"Equal parts informative, vulnerable, practical and laugh-out-loud funny, *The
Inside Scoop on Eating Disorder Recovery* is a wonderful addition to the eating
disorder books on the market. I loved this book and I know it is going to help
so many!"

Amanda White, LPC, Owner of Therapy for Women

"With focused self-reflection activities and deeply personal stories of recovery,
this book is like a manual on 'how to be kind to your body' at every step of
healing! You will feel seen, heard, and valued through each and every turn of
the page as you take back your well-being."

Rebecca Scritchfield, RDN, Author of *Body Kindness*

"The pro-recovery messages that Jennifer and Colleen tirelessly work to put
into the world help so many people find their own voice to shout back at their
eating disorder with. This book feels like having two best friends fighting
there with you (who just happen to be armed with sh*t tonnes of research,
qualifications and personal experience, too). It's accessible, inclusive and
encouraging, and I can see it being a starting point to the peace that everyone
in recovery deserves to find with food, movement and their bodies."

Megan Jayne Crabbe, Author of *Body Positive Power*

"Inspirational and fiercely anti-diet culture! This book is digestible and accessible to all, and takes the reader beyond words into journal prompts and

activities to create action in their recovery. A must read for anyone struggling or supporting a loved one who is struggling with an eating disorder!"

Haley Goodrich, RD, LDN, CEDRD, Founder/Clinical Director of INSPIRD Nutrition

"*The Inside Scoop on Eating Disorder Recovery* is a fantastic addition to the eating disorder self help resource collection. Two recovered therapists share lessons learned in their own recovery processes, include thoughtful voices from other recovery perspectives, and bring their therapeutic excellence to the page. This book is full of resources, thoughtful reflection questions, and invites readers to engage in critical steps toward recovery, in a way that is both meaningful and measurable. I look forward to sharing this book with my clients and am very happy to be able to recommend *The Inside Scoop* as a resource to humans who are in the recovery process, with and without additional therapeutic support. This book is a gift."

Anna Sweeney, MS, RD, LDN, CEDRD-S, Owner of Whole Life Nutrition

"*The Inside Scoop on Eating Disorder Recovery: Advice from Two Therapists Who Have Been There* is a must-read for any client struggling with an eating disorder or for anyone supporting a loved one in their eating disorder recovery. The authors are experts in the field and their knowledge, understanding, compassion, and desire to support clients in recovery shines through. They are funny, inspiring, relatable, and provide wonderful insight into diet culture, health at every size, and body image, along with skills and journal prompts to incorporate in the eating disorder recovery process. I cannot speak highly enough of this book and will be recommending this to all my clients and colleagues."

Laura Deneen, LPC-MHSP, NCC, Founder of Anchored Counseling Company

"*The Inside Scoop on Eating Disorder Recovery* shares TANGIBLE advice, education and inspiration for people in recovery. Recovery from an eating disorder is a long journey, and unfortunately we live in a society with lots of triggers. The authors provide a map. They get it from a scientific perspective, and they get it because they've been there. I highly recommend this book to anyone struggling with an eating disorder who wants their life back."

Kristina Saffran, Founder of Project HEAL

"If you can call a book on eating disorder recovery fun and witty, this is it! Colleen and Jennifer take you into their eating disorder brains, share their stories of recovery, and offer actionable steps you can take to start healing yourself today. It's comprehensive, backed by research, and delivered like you're chatting with two friends. If you're struggling with an eating disorder, or want to heal your relationship with food and your body, this book is for you!"

Nicole Cruz, MS, RDN

The Inside Scoop on Eating Disorder Recovery

The Inside Scoop on Eating Disorder Recovery is a fresh, smart, how-to book that helps people with eating disorders to heal their relationship with food, their bodies, and ultimately themselves.

Written from the perspective of two eating disorder therapists, both of whom are recovered from their own eating disorders, the text uses humor, personal narratives, and research-proven techniques to offer specific action-able guidelines on how to reclaim one's life from an eating disorder. The authors explain the difference between dieting and eating disorders, break down the stages of recovery, and provide tips on how to thrive in each stage. The book provides powerful myth-busting on topics that have histor-ically not been addressed in eating disorder recovery books, such as clean eating and orthorexia, exercising in recovery, and fat positivity. Tangible exercises at the end of each chapter provide readers with advice and tips on implementing this approach to recovery in their day-to-day lives.

The humorous and down-to-earth tone of the book creates an authentic and genuine feel that leaves those who struggle with chronic dieting, eating disorders, and negative body image feeling connected and heard.

Colleen Reichmann, PsyD, is a licensed clinical psychologist residing in Philadelphia, PA. She specializes in the treatment of eating disorders and has been named as one of the top eating disorder experts in the country.

Jennifer Rollin, MSW, LCSW-C, is an eating disorder therapist and founder of The Eating Disorder Center. She has been interviewed speaking about eating disorders on ABC, NBC, PBS, and Fox. She has been named as one of the top eating disorder experts in the country.

The Inside Scoop on Eating Disorder Recovery

Advice from Two Therapists
Who Have Been There

Colleen Reichmann and Jennifer Rollin

Routledge
Taylor & Francis Group

NEW YORK AND LONDON

First published 2021
by Routledge
605 Third Avenue, New York, NY 10158

and by Routledge
2 Park Square, Milton Park, Abingdon, Oxon OX14 4RN

Routledge is an imprint of the Taylor & Francis Group, an informa business

Library of Congress Cataloging-in-Publication Data
Names: Reichmann, Colleen, author. | Rollin, Jennifer, author.
Title: The inside scoop on eating disorder recovery : advice from two
therapists who have been there / Colleen Reichmann, Jennifer Rollin.
Description: New York, NY : Routledge, 2021. |
Includes bibliographical references and index. |
Identifiers: LCCN 2020041431 (print) | LCCN 2020041432 (ebook) |
ISBN 9780367703646 (hardback) | ISBN 9780367900816 (paperback) |
ISBN 9781003022480 (ebook)
Subjects: LCSH: Eating disorders–Treatment–Popular works.
Classification: LCC RC552.E18 R45 2021 (print) |
LCC RC552.E18 (ebook) | DDC 616.85/2606–dc23
LC record available at https://lccn.loc.gov/2020041431
LC ebook record available at https://lccn.loc.gov/2020041432

ISBN: 978-0-367-70364-6 (hbk)
ISBN: 978-0-367-90081-6 (pbk)
ISBN: 978-1-003-02248-0 (ebk)

Typeset in Times New Roman
by Newgen Publishing UK

Colleen
To Ezra: Before I knew you, I fought for you. You are and always have been my reason for recovery (even when I didn't realize it).

Jennifer
To Mark: Thank you for being the most amazing and supportive person. I love you so much! To my parents: Thank you for standing by me through so many difficult moments. I am incredibly grateful to have you in my life.

Colleen and Jennifer:
To all of the wonderful, wise, colorful souls out there who are struggling with an eating disorder: We see you. We are cheering you on. This one's for you.

Content warning

This book delves into how to recover from an eating disorder. We (your authors) share personal tidbits from our own journeys with eating disorder recovery. Five guest authors share details about their respective journeys in Chapter 8. There are no numbers referenced anywhere in the text. However, behaviors such as bingeing, purging, restricting, and over-exercising are mentioned at various points throughout the book. Additionally, we describe research that uses the words "obesity" and "overweight" at various points in this text. We believe that these terms are stigmatizing and fat-phobic, and hence only use them when quoting research. They will appear in the text as "o*esity" and "o*erweight." While we have done our damndest to keep the content as non-triggering as possible, we want readers to have this information upfront, in order to make an informed decision about proceeding. Please do what is best for you and your recovery.

Disclaimer

This book details the authors' personal experiences with, and opinions about, eating disorders, including different treatment and recovery approaches. It is designed to provide helpful information on the subjects discussed. This book is not meant to be used, nor should it be used, to diagnose or treat any medical or mental health condition. For diagnosis or treatment of any medical or mental health condition, please consult your own physician and/or therapist.

This book is not intended as a substitute for consultation with a licensed healthcare practitioner, such as your physician or therapist. Before you begin any healthcare program, or change your lifestyle in anyway, you should consult your physician and/or licensed healthcare practitioner to ensure that the recommendations contained in this book will not harm you.

The publisher and the authors are not responsible for any specific health conditions that may require medical supervision and are not liable for any damages or negative consequences from any treatment or other action by any person reading or following the information in this book. References and other information are provided for informational and educational purposes only and do not constitute endorsement of any websites or other sources.

Although the publisher and the authors have made every effort to ensure that the information in this book was correct at press time, and while this publication is designed to provide accurate information in regard to the subject matters covered, the publisher and the authors assume no responsibility for errors, inaccuracies, omissions, or any other inconsistencies herein and hereby disclaim any liability to any party for any loss, damage, or disruption caused by errors or omissions, whether such errors or omissions result from negligence, accident, or any other cause.

No warranties or guarantees are expressed or implied by the publisher's and/or authors' choice to include any of the content in this book. Neither the publisher nor authors shall be liable for any physical, psychological, emotional, financial, or commercial damages, including, but not limited to, special, incidental, consequential or other damages. You acknowledge that you are responsible for your own choices, actions, and results.

Contents

Biographies

Dr. Colleen Reichmann is a licensed clinical psychologist who specializes in the treatment of eating disorders, body image issues, self-injury, and trauma. She is the founder of her private practice, Therapy for Eating Disorders and Body Image, where she sees clients (in Philadelphia PA).

Colleen completed her predoctoral internship at the University Medical Center of Princeton at Plainsboro Center for Eating Disorders. She then worked as a postdoctoral fellow at Sheppard Pratt Center for Eating Disorders. In both of these programs, she worked across the inpatient, partial hospitalization, and IOP levels of care. She then went on to create eating disorder programming at the College of William and Mary.

Colleen is a prominent speaker and writer. She has spoken at numerous regional and national eating disorder conferences, and various universities, treatment centers and retreats. She has written for Scary Mommy, Recovery Warriors, MoreLove, Project HEAL, The Mighty, and more.

Colleen is an advocate for the Health at Every Size® and fat positivity movements, and was recently named one of the top eating disorder experts in the country by a prominent eating disorder treatment center.

And lastly (but perhaps most importantly), Colleen has recovered from anorexia (after years of being the patient that most therapists dreaded working with ... seriously – picture arms folded, annoyed expression, and sarcastic responses). Her struggle with an eating disorder and subsequent recovery have led her to her passion of spreading awareness about eating disorders, and helping others to heal.

Jennifer Rollin is a therapist and founder of The Eating Disorder Center, an outpatient group therapy and coaching practice, who specializes in working with adolescents and adults with eating disorders including anorexia, bulimia, and binge eating disorder, body image issues, anxiety, and depression. Jennifer is also an advocate for the Health at Every Size® and fat positivity movements.

Jennifer has experience working in a variety of settings including an outpatient mental health clinic, residential programs for adolescents, and a sexual assault crisis hotline. She served as the chairwoman of Project Heal's national network of eating disorder treatment providers. She received a Best of Rockville Award for 2019 under the category of psychotherapists. Jennifer has been named as one of the top eating disorder experts in the country by a prominent eating disorder treatment center.

Jennifer has a certificate in Enhanced Cognitive Behavioral Therapy for Eating Disorders. She also has a certificate in Dialectical Behavior Therapy. She is a Certified Intuitive Eating Counselor. She was on The Junior Board of Directors for The National Eating Disorders Association. She was invited to serve on the conference committee for The National Eating Disorders Association's 2018 Conference.

Jennifer has been interviewed speaking about eating disorders on television including on Fox, ABC, PBS and NBC. She has also been interviewed by *The Washington Post*, *TIME* Magazine, *US News & World Report*, *Forbes*, *The Huffington Post*, *Seventeen* Magazine, *In Style* Magazine, and *Esquire* Magazine. She gives talks about eating disorders at national eating disorder conferences, therapy centers, retreats, and colleges.

She is an expert writer on *The Huffington Post* and *Psychology Today*. Her professional blog was named one of the top eating disorder blogs in the world.

Her articles have reached thousands of people through websites, magazines, and books, including *Eating Disorders in America: A Reference Handbook*, *How To Thrive: Expert Tips For Recovering From An Eating Disorder*, EatingDisorderHope.com, Anxiety.org, NationalEating Disorders. org, and *Social Work Today* Magazine.

She is personally recovered from her own battle with an eating disorder and this has inspired her passion for helping others to find freedom from eating disorders. She is so grateful to get to do this work.

Acknowledgments

There are just too many people to thank. That's how we both feel as we sit down to write our acknowledgments. Too many people who have helped each of us claw our way out of the hell that is an eating disorder. Too many people who have assisted with this particular project. We don't even know where to begin!

To Amanda Devine: Thank you for believing in us.

To Shira, Kaitlin, Nia, Aaron, and Katie: Thank you for graciously gifting this book with each of your stories in the fat positivity chapter. Your voices are so needed.

To Nicole: Thank you for being an editing wizard. Thank you for reviewing every chapter, giving such great feedback, and always being there to offer a kind and encouraging word.

Colleen

First and foremost – To Jen: Thank you for being my recovery soul sister. For never ever judging me. For being the best project and writing partner that I could ever ask for. For being the person who I know I can call when everything is falling apart. One of the best things about this career is that it brought you into my life.

To Joe: The biggest cheerleader that I have ever had. Thank you for supporting me while I wrote this book. Thank you for seeing me and loving me. I don't know what I did to deserve you but it must have been something pretty good.

To Mom: Thank you for always being the mom that makes cupcakes with real sugar. You believed in food freedom before it was in vogue. I am so lucky to have you as a mom.

To Dad: Thank you sticking by my side through it all. Thank you for inspiring me to write this book. The world is anxiously waiting for you to write yours!

To Katie: Thank you for rooting me on while I wrote this book. Forever the little sister that I look up to.

To Sarah: Thank you for being the friend that has kept showing up, even when I was at my lowest points. I would never have made it out of college alive without ya. You truly are the most loyal, beautiful soul. Thank you for believing in this book, and being the "proud friend." ("Here's our star!")

And finally: to all of my former and current clients. To every single patient I ever worked with at Princeton House Behavioral Health Eating Disorders Unit, and Sheppard Pratt Center for Eating Disorders. To every student that I worked with at the College of William and Mary. To every single one of the clients I work with now. You all have given me so much more than I could ever give you. It is an absolute honor to walk or have walked beside you on this journey.

Jennifer

There were so many people who helped me in preparation of this book and I am incredibly grateful for them.

To Colleen: My soul-sister and one of my best friends. Thank you for co-authoring this book with me, and always being someone I could go to if I was feeling stressed, and for being so collaborative throughout the process. I truly wouldn't have wanted to write this book with anyone else! I am beyond grateful to have you in my life.

To Mark: Thank you for providing emotional support throughout the writing process and for being my constant cheerleader. I love you more than I can say. You are one of the best people I've ever met.

To My Parents: Thank you for always believing in me and my potential. Thank you for being the first to offer – whenever I need help with anything. I am lucky to have such supportive parents.

To Megan: Thank you for helping me out so much with the references, which took a big stressor off of me and was so appreciated.

To My amazing team at The Eating Disorder Center: Thank you for (as always) believing in me and cheering me on. I am thankful to work with such an incredible team of clinicians.

To my incredible clients: Thank you for inspiring me every day with your courage and bravery in working on your eating disorder recovery. It is an honor to work with you and I'm so incredibly grateful to be able to do this work.

Introduction

Why We Wrote This Book

Hello there friends! Thanks for cracking this puppy open. Welcome to your all-inclusive guide to healing from an eating disorder. Why did we write this book? Well, to answer this question, we are going to call upon a tidbit of wisdom from *The West Wing* (yup, the show):

> This guy's walking down the street when he falls in a hole. The walls are so steep he can't get out. A doctor passes by and the guy shouts up, 'Hey you. Can you help me out?' The doctor writes a prescription, throws it down in the hole and moves on. Then a priest comes along and the guy shouts up, 'Father, I'm down in this hole can you help me out?' The priest writes out a prayer, throws it down in the hole and moves on. Then a friend walks by, 'Hey, Joe, it's me can you help me out?' And the friend jumps in the hole. Our guy says, 'Are you stupid? Now we're both down here.' The friend says, 'Yeah, but I've been down here before and I know the way out.'
>
> (Sorkin & Schlamme, 2000)

Right there. That is why we wrote this. Because we have both suffered from consuming, miserable eating disorders of our own. We are the guys in the hole who know the way out. We took on this project because we wanted to share what we have learned through our own recovery processes, years of education (i.e. riding that grad school struggle bus), and through our work with others whom we have helped to fully recover.

We are in the interesting position of being professionals in the eating disorder field who have personal histories with the very illness that we now treat. As eating disorder therapists, we both have a ton of training that helped us in developing the strategies that we write about in this book. We've taken the classes. We've done the research. Yawn. (Ok not really, we're actually research nerds – don't tell anyone.) We have the fancy degrees and letters behind our names. However; our real training, our *soul training*, as we like to call it, comes from our own past struggles. We have fought tooth and nail to claw our way out of the eating disorder hole. The fight was long, tiring, and complex for both of us (for different reasons that we will totally let you in on). We both felt hopeless at various points. We both doubted our ability to fully recover. And yet, we did it. We took back the power from our eating disorders, and changed our lives. Now we are jumping back down into that hole to help *you* claw *your* way out.

Throughout this book, you will read about research-proven methods to help you overcome your eating disorder. We will also provide practical strategies that have worked for the many people that we have treated. We will offer pieces from our own journeys along the way – little tidbits about how we struggled and what *actually* helped.

Side note: This book is *not* just for people with a diagnosis of an eating disorder. In fact, it doesn't really matter to us if you have a formal diagnosis. Why? Because research tells us that a huge amount of people who struggle with disordered eating never receive the diagnosis and treatment that they deserve. If you struggle with your relationship with food, then this book is for you. Maybe you've been riding that damn dieting roller coaster for years, without any formal diagnosis – this book is for you. If you've never sought treatment because you have concerns that you aren't "sick enough" – this book is for you. If your struggles have been invalidated by a professional who said that your weight isn't low enough to have an eating disorder, or that your symptoms are not "severe enough" – this book is for you. If you are living in a larger body, a smaller body, or an "in-between" body – this book is for you. If you restrict, binge, purge, use laxatives, chew and spit out your food, or compulsively exercise – this book is for you. You get the picture, right? This book is for anyone who struggles. We want to be very clear about this. It is for *anyone* who wants to find peace in their body.

We don't ask that you be totally on board with every single one of our strategies right away. All that we ask is that you keep an open mind and a spark of hope – you know, that small voice that occasionally prompts the ever-so-important thought: "maybe I *can* feel better." That voice is your inner badass – we're going to help you harness that shit.

This book is not a substitute for professional treatment. It is meant more as an adjunct to treatment. It is important to contact an eating disorder professional, if you haven't already done so, and obtain a thorough physical and psychiatric evaluation and recommendations for moving forward. We suggest working with a Health At Every Size® (HAES®)-informed eating disorder therapist and dietitian in addition to reading this book.

We hope that this book helps you on your journey. Now put on your helmet, knee pads and sunglasses and buckle up – it's gonna be a bumpy and worthwhile (!) ride.

Colleen's Story

The first thing people who have not had an eating disorder tend to ask is "did you always hate food?" The answer to this question is NO (accompanied by an eye roll). I did not "always hate food." In fact, even when

I was in the depths of my eating disorder, I did not "hate food." It is a myth that folks with eating disorders dislike food (to be discussed later on y'all).

As a child, I can recall eating joyfully. Let me pause for a moment to note the HUGE amount of privilege that I grew up with. My nuclear family is white and can generally be described as upper middle class. Because we never struggled financially, food scarcity was not something that we had to deal with. (This is a massive privilege. Food scarcity can be a trigger for eating disorders later in life.) Also, because we are white, my family never had to learn to live through the trauma of racism and oppression that Black people and people of color must endure in this country every day. Racism and white supremacy are at the root of many people's eating disorders. And finally, I and most of my family members live in average and small-sized bodies. We never suffered through the trauma that fat folks have to deal with every day due to the rampant fatphobia in this county. I note this privilege because it is important for you to know that my story is just that – very privileged. There are deeper elements of oppression that contribute to disordered eating for many, many individuals that my story won't touch. I cannot and should not pretend to understand these elements while telling my story. But please know, they will be touched upon later on in this book.

My mom is and always has been a m-fin' boss in the kitchen. She cooked homemade dinners for her family every evening, and even routinely whipped up cakes, cookies, and other white-sugar-filled (*gasp*) delicacies for everyone to enjoy. I have memories of the five of us (my two siblings, mom, dad, and myself) sitting around the kitchen table at night with sticky fingers, licking buttercream frosting off of a chocolate scratch cupcake, silence filling the room because we were all so absorbed in our desserts.

Prior to puberty, I wasn't a picky eater. I wasn't fearful of food. I wasn't hateful towards my body. In fact, I don't remember having too many thoughts about my body at that time (ahem – privilege alert). It was just a thing – a thing that I existed in. Not good. Not bad. Just was.

However, lest I paint too carefree of a picture of myself, there are other things I want you to be aware of as I tell you my story. I was genetically loaded to develop an eating disorder. I mean that quite literally – my paternal grandmother struggled with anorexia throughout her entire life. She obsessively talked about cutting calories and staying thin throughout my father's childhood, and into her 50s, 60s, and 70s. In fact, her favorite topic remained weight and how to avoid eating up until dementia set in, and even longer – she spoke about this until dementia took her voice. Only when she stopped speaking and truly stopped being able to think coherently did she finally stop obsessing over thinness. Sad huh?

So basically, I came with this *thing* in me – this genetically passed ability to become immersed and obsessed with control. Lucky me. This gene set was apparent from a pretty early age. My mom likes to tell the tale of how I, at four years old, kindly suggested that she should load the dishwasher in a more organized manner. When I took a look at the dishwasher later that day, I glanced up at her sadly and said, "I'm really disappointed that you failed to follow my system." (Alarm bells anyone? Ma? C'mon now.)

Another legend from my childhood is from my years taking ballet. Once, during a recital, a few of the ballerinas made a mistake during the routine and got our tutus all tangled up and stuck. The audience began laughing good naturedly. The other girls laughed nervously along, but I, serious ballerina that I was, apparently squared myself off towards the audience, put my hands on my hips and frowned, as if to say – take us *seriously*! I was in preschool. (More alarm bells, right?)

That was my personality. Perfectionistic, controlling, achievement oriented, attentive to detail, and harm-avoidant. I was also shy. Very, *very* shy. This shyness impacted my social skills. I have report cards from elementary school that say, "Colleen does very well in reading and writing, but struggles to make friends. She picks a 'representative' to talk for her during circle time."

I think my perfectionism, obsessive nature, and shyness all combined to create an inability to make friends easily, which in turn contributed to my developing pretty low self-esteem. Some issues within my family also exacerbated this low self-esteem. As a middle child, I found myself having thoughts along the lines of "do I belong in this family?" as well as "this family would be better off without me" quite a bit. (This is not meant to put blame on my parents. I was independent by nature, and my "I'll do it myself" attitude likely contributed to personal feelings of loneliness in my family system.) My self-worth began to plummet as I progressed through second grade, to third grade, and finally bottomed out around fourth grade. This is when I can recall first having the thought, "I hate myself."

But wait – it gets better! (sarcasm) Upon arriving to the magical land that we call middle school, I hit puberty. BAM. Just like that, before most of my peers. Hips. Boobs. Zits. My new school felt Darwinian and terrifying in the best of circumstances – but to have to show up every day like *that*? Oily, awkward, and completely unsure of how to navigate my new body? It was unbearable.

Some bullying started around this time. Kids on the bus said cruel things about my appearance. My brother's friends made fun of my quiet nature. And two (asshole) boys, whose faces I can recall to this day, called me an "amazon. And not in good way" (referring to my height).

I didn't know what to do. I didn't have the emotional resources to handle this type of bullying. My self-worth was already rock bottom, I was already terrified to talk to my peers – life felt out of control and agonizing. So, I imploded.

I turned inward and searched for something – anything – to channel my angst and controlling nature into. And, being that I was growing up in the 90s, when the thin ideal was blatant (Kate Moss was the favored model, and the "grapefruit diet" was still en vogue), dieting seemed like the obvious choice. I began tracking calories and "cutting down." I slipped down the slope hard and fast. By the end of middle school, my (sole two) friends were *begging* me to stop talking about calories and how big I was. I, of course, did not listen. High school was fast approaching, and I wanted nothing more than for my life to be different. Thinness seemed like the fastest route to different, so onward and forward.

High school *was* different, in some respects. I purchased some new clothing, overcame some elements of my crippling lack of confidence, and managed to make a few friends. Bought some short jean skirts and clunky Steve Madden sandals. (What's up fellow millennials?) I admired the cool, popular people, but never achieved said rank. But I did begin dating. By the end of freshman year, I had myself a shiny new boyfriend. Things were looking up? Maybe?

On the outside, yes. But on the inside, things were sort of chugging along in the same manner. I still hated myself. I still felt depressed more often than not. I still felt consumed with the idea that thinness would bring happiness. Now it is important to mention here again that I was objectively moderately thin. Even though I was bullied a bit for the weight gain that came with puberty, I never lived in a larger body. My body throughout high school was very much average-sized. I knew this. Cognitively. But I was consumed with the desire to be "ultra-thin." I recall craving to be so thin that people would ask, "is she ok?"

I chased weight loss all throughout high school. I began running track because I thought it would help me lose weight. I kept a "calorie journal." I stuck pictures of thin models in my binders to "inspire me." And on, and on, and on.

When college finally rolled around, I felt ill-prepared. My self-esteem was fragile at best, rock bottom at worst. I had stopped learning how to handle distress years ago – replacing learning to sit with discomfort with calorie counting and running. And yet, I packed my bags with the rest of 'em and off I went – journeying a whole two hours from home to a place that would nearly kill me.

What do you think about when the word "college" comes to mind? Wild parties? Late night study sessions? Hung-over brunches with housemates? When I think about college, one word comes to mind: hunger.

Picture this: a highly sensitive, insecure 18-year-old, with an undiagnosed eating disorder, away from home for the first time, thrust into an environment of constant partying, increased work load, and other dormmates with their own eating disorders. I had viewed going away to college as the panacea for all of the issues that I had struggled with in high school. In hindsight, it was silly for me to think that my problems wouldn't follow me.

I found my freshman year to be one of the loneliest experiences of my life. Try as I might, I simply did not connect with the girls that were in my dorm hall. I felt ill at ease at parties – unsure, uncool, and, to my dismay, STILL OILY. Being unsure about who I was and feeling as though I didn't fit in – these were big, scary problems – not something that I was at all ready to tackle as an 18-year-old scared kid. So, I turned inward again.

Terrified of the "freshman 15," I began to engage in an even more structured practice of daily food and calorie logging. Food logging led to restricting food groups. Restricting food groups led to bingeing on my roommates' snacks at night. Bingeing at night led to purging in the weird, one-person bathroom on the basement level of the dorm building. Yada yada yada. Let's just put it this way – if it is considered an "eating disorder behavior," I did it in college. A lot.

What had started as a desperate attempt to increase my self-esteem and quell icky feelings escalated into a cycle of disordered eating that led to feelings of absolute *self-loathing*. I had lost a great deal of weight. (PS – no, I will never share numbers in this book. Numbers are NEVER helpful to the discussion of eating disorders.) My body changed enough to garner attention from family members, professors and friends. I started seeing a therapist and was diagnosed with anorexia nervosa. People were FINALLY wondering "is she ok?" So why did I still feel so empty?

While the weight loss was alarming, the truly scary side effect of all of this was on my mood, which plummeted freshman year, and remained unstable all throughout the next three years. I became chronically suicidal. On the worst days, I woke up, only to take a sleeping pill moments later. Being awake felt like too much to bear.

I have snippets of memories. Freshman year – tears silently rolling down my cheeks as I sat in the backseat of the car while my parents drove me back to school after winter break. Sophomore year – running on a treadmill, desperately trying to proactively compensate because I had agreed to go get ice cream that night with friends. Junior and senior year – restricting during the day and then drinking my weight in alcohol later that evening, only to wake up in in the morning, vomiting and depressed. Though I had made some really amazing friends, and cherish my time with them, these darker memories *are* college to me.

You must be thinking, "Why didn't you get help?" The thing is, I *did* get help. Like I said – my parents, friends, even professors approached me with concern off and on throughout those four years. There were trips to the hospital, appointments with various therapists, dietitians and all different types and levels of treatment – this is what getting help for an eating disorder can look like sometimes.

For me, it looked like getting up and then falling down again. It looked like gaining weight and acting like all is well so that people left me alone. It looked like planning to relapse while eating dinner with my roommates. It looked like disappearing for weeks on end over the summers, and then laughing about it with friends in the fall – "Sorry about that. My 'summer diet' got the best of me again." It looked like waking up Saturday mornings with no memory of last night, because I was dangerously intoxicated after drinking on an empty stomach, and then rolling out the door to lie about how I was doing in therapy. My recovery trajectory, like the majority of those who struggle with eating disorders, was non-linear to say the least.

Somehow, miraculously, I graduated. I pulled myself together and decided that graduate school sounded like a good bet. I applied and was accepted into a clinical psychology doctoral program with one goal in mind: become an eating disorder researcher.

My recovery was held together by a loosely tied bow when I entered graduate school. I guess it's no wonder that I relapsed *hard* by the end of the first year. This relapse was due to a perfect storm – competition and mean-spiritedness from the other students in my cohort, sexual harassment from a supervisor, the soul-sucking nature of graduate school, and the fact that I just generally did not have my shit together yet.

The grad school relapse was interesting because it looked different from before. This time, I was consumed with "wellness." Gym trips to "be kind to myself." Raw food eating regimens because "toxins." Fruit-free, vegetable-filled smoothies (*gag*) because "this is about taking care of myself. I don't care about weight anymore." The sneaky wellness craze snuck up on me, and I, as someone who has a vulnerability for an eating disorder, got sucked right back in. It took a good amount of time for me to recognize this and crawl my way back out, yet again.

There was no magic recovery bullet – no light bulb moment that I can pinpoint in terms of how I reached full recovery after that. Just a slow crawl towards trying to live with the same voracity that I had tried to die. All the usual suspects – therapy, consistent meals, weight gain, healthier relationships – these things helped me in that crawl towards life.

I also had something else on my side. Something new – a sense of purpose. I wanted to be the best damn eating disorder researcher out there. And I knew that to do this, I needed to be healed. Weight gain happened (yet again), but this time, alongside of it, I started actually telling the truth to my therapist. The all-consuming fear of gaining weight dissipated. I began to fill my life with more important things to focus on other than my body.

At some point, years into my training, I decided to work with college students who were struggling with body image. This work inevitably led to me working with students who had eating disorders (once I felt ready). And then *everything just clicked*. I loved the work. I got it. I empathized with these students in a deep way. I realized that this empathy led to nonjudgment, and that the work I did was good! It only seemed right to continue forward with my new career goal: become an eating disorders psychologist.

And become an eating disorders psychologist I did! I completed an internship and fellowship at two renowned inpatient treatment centers. The work felt natural. It still does. This is my passion, and my calling. I have unending empathy for those who struggle with eating disorders.

Now, what's important to note here is that just because I had an eating disorder does not mean I understand YOUR eating disorder. All it does is afford me empathy. My schooling and years in practice have helped me to figure out the different ways in which to help folks who are struggling (ways that I'll be sharing with you throughout this book – don't say I never did anything for ya). But when it comes down to it, everyone's eating disorder is different. My recovery journey looks different from Jennifer's. Her recovery will look different from yours. If you really want to recover, you'll have to find the right combination of skills, support systems, and motivating factors for YOU. I'm here to help with that. I know you can do it.

Jennifer's Story

I knew about the concept of "good" and "bad" foods (hello diet culture!) from a pretty early age.

However, as a child and through the majority of my teenage years, I simply didn't care if I ate foods that I knew society deemed as "bad." In fact, my inner rebel actually sought them out even more (because I sure as heck didn't like being told what to do).

Now let me just pause for a second to talk about privilege. We will explain more on this topic later but I think it's important to acknowledge here that like Colleen, I grew up in an upper middle-class white family and had a lot of privilege. I did not have to deal with issues like food insecurity and poverty, the trauma of being in a larger body in a fat-phobic culture, or racism faced by Black individuals and people of color. These factors can greatly contribute towards the development of disordered eating and eating disorders. Due to my own privilege, I can never claim to understand the experiences of more marginalized individuals.

I enjoyed food. It didn't take up much mental space in my head. And I was a big fan of dessert. I remember that my favorite book that I would ask my mom to read to me over and over was called "Minnie and Mickie Mouse's Picnic." I remember practically drooling over the description of the lemonade and the chocolate cake that Minnie and Mickie Mouse ate.

While food and body image stuff wouldn't be a major issue until later, anxiety was a struggle for me starting from an early age. I also had early issues with low self-worth and feeling "ugly" at times in comparison to the other kids. I didn't realize then how the perfect storm – the one that would eventually cause my eating disorder to develop – was ever so slowly starting to brew.

When I was in the third grade my parents sat me down and told me that they had made the decision to send me to private school. I was pissed. I was upset to leave behind my friends and to start somewhere new. Fourth grade at the new school was rough. I was incredibly socially anxious and spent recess in the classroom with my teacher. She called my parents and said that she was concerned because I didn't play with the other kids. Eventually, with Joanne's (shout out to my badass fourth grade teacher!) encouragement I started to branch out and made a small group of friends. Still, I continued to struggle with lots of school related anxiety.

Let's flash forward to high school. A scene I will never forget: I am an intimidated freshman starting at a new school. I have my duffel bag all packed. My mom pulls up to the parking lot in her big white Honda and I nervously get out – lugging my heavy duffel bag alongside me. The school's way of getting everyone acquainted was called "The Ninth Grade Camping Trip" where much to my dismay (as someone who was rarely outdoors), I would be expected to hike, camp and canoe with all of my future classmates and some teacher chaperones. Let's just say that this wasn't my idea of a good time. *At all.*

It's no surprise that I had a hard time making friends in high school, as I totally didn't fit in with the crowd that attended the small private high school I had chosen.

I remember feeling awkward, insecure and ugly. I had buckteeth, "uncool clothes," frizzy hair, and a body that wasn't as thin as some of the other girls (despite having thin privilege). I was also bullied by some of the "popular girls." I had maybe one or two friends for the majority of high school. I felt like there was something deeply wrong with me. I coped with all of this by completely throwing myself into musical theatre. Through theatre, I could step into the role of someone else. Thus, escaping from my uncomfortable, awkward, and generally unhappy state.

I participated in around 13 musicals and plays in middle and high school. This is where my high achievement and tendency towards perfectionism first manifested. I practiced singing ALL of the time (much to the dismay of my high school teachers!) and really threw myself into whatever role I was playing. My best friend from middle school still jokes about how I went as far as coloring my eyebrows red to play the role of Annie. I was hyper focused on getting a "good part" in musicals and nothing else really mattered to me.

Musical theatre was the only area where I felt like I excelled and got praise from others and it was also a convenient escape from reality. It was the one place in the world where I felt like I fit in.

Senior year of high school, I finally made a group of actual friends but also picked up the habit of drinking and abusing prescription pills (clearly escaping reality had become my thing).

I constantly compared myself to my extremely thin (and sought after by boys) group of friends. I was also very anxious about the transition into college and felt like I needed something else to "focus on." I decided to go on a diet and began restricting my food.

One of my close friends was prescribed Adderall and one day I asked her if I could try it. Very quickly, I was hooked. Not only did Adderall enable me to escape my mood issues and insecurities, it also caused me to completely lose my appetite. Soon I was taking Adderall every day and I was losing weight rapidly. I also started weighing myself obsessively. At the time, everyone congratulated me for losing weight – the praise was addictive.

However, I was faced with a harsh reality when a concerned peer went to my guidance counselor and told her I was abusing prescription pills. Cut to my dad storming into the drama room while I was in the middle of class, demanding that I exit immediately. He left and I remember throwing the robin's egg blue pouch filled with pills into the changing room and then meeting him on the lawn in front of the performing arts building where he and my mom stood dumping my backpack out onto the grass.

They didn't find the pills that day, but I decided to come clean anyway. Once I did, I was scared enough about potential consequences that I quit the pills and was able to resume eating normally. I didn't know it then but this little exercise in self-starvation would be a foreshadowing of what was to come.

I went to college at American University, where I escaped from myself by drinking heavily. My freshman year of college I had a bad breakup and was set up with someone by a mutual friend. On our third date, he raped me. I was intensely depressed and suicidal after that and continued to drink heavily to try to cope with my emotions. I quickly spiraled and hit rock bottom with my alcohol use and suicidal thoughts.

After things pretty much fell apart, I decided that I was going to turn it all around. I focused on getting straight A's in school and basically lived at the library. Just as I had poured everything into musical theatre, I put my heart and soul into getting good grades. (I was definitely *way* too obsessive about it. Shocker, I know.)

I had gained weight and I remember the moment clearly when I went to try on a formal dress for an event. I hated how I looked in it and told myself that I was going to try to "lose weight in a healthy way" (spoiler alert: this went terribly).

It started out looking more like orthorexia. I began exercising regularly for the first time in my life and eating only what I deemed to be "healthy foods." I posted pictures on social media of brown rice, chicken, and vegetables. It quickly spiraled out of control into an eating disorder that completely consumed my life and I was eventually diagnosed with anorexia nervosa.

After I was diagnosed, a very close family member sat me down and told me that she had a history of struggling with an eating disorder. I had the genetics, the temperamental traits (hello anxiety, rigidity, and perfectionism!), and a trauma history. In hindsight, it was the perfect storm of factors that came together for me to develop an eating disorder.

At the worst of my illness, I was so terrified of eating at restaurants (because God forbid, they cook something in oil or *gasp* butter!) that I felt like it was a phobia. I became depressed, obsessed with my weight, addicted to exercise, and my every waking through was about food and weight. It was exhausting.

My eating disorder was a shape shifter. It started as orthorexia, then anorexia with moments of bingeing and purging, then to a "fitness and clean lifestyle obsession." I started attending outpatient treatment with eating disorder specialists and remember asking my dietitian to eat desserts with me every week. In the beginning, I felt pretty motivated to recover, but in different stages of my journey I felt varying levels of motivation.

It's hard to summarize all of the treatment, struggles, tears, and "recovery wins" into a short narrative. My journey was definitely NOT linear (none really are) and I had a few pretty rough relapses along the way.

What changed the game for me was when I stumbled upon the Health at Every Size® movement on Facebook. Being raised in diet culture this gave me a perspective I had never considered. I became aware of my own thin privilege and the fat-phobic views of my therapist at the time.

It took lots of therapy and dietitian sessions, but eventually things got better and better. I used my obsessive traits and high achieving personality "for good" and threw my all into recovery. At the end of senior year, I decided to go to graduate school to become a therapist (never thinking I'd become an eating disorder therapist!).

I did two clinical practicums during my graduate work and found that I naturally gravitated towards and did great work with the clients struggling with eating disorders. My own experience has given me a sense of empathy and a deeper understanding of eating disorders – but I never relied on my own journey as a roadmap for my clients, as everyone is unique. Instead, I pursued advanced training in the treatment of eating disorders.

After graduate school, I worked for three years at a residential program for adolescent girls with eating disorders, mood disorders, and trauma histories. From there I opened my own private practice and then years later my group practice, The Eating Disorder Center.

I truly LOVE this work. I feel that my professional calling is helping people to recover from eating disorders. I can't picture doing anything else and while it's not an "easy" job it is so incredibly rewarding to see people fully recover.

Flash forward to present day. "Do you want pancakes for breakfast?" my fiancé asks. "Sure," I reply without a second thought. We eat pancakes dripping with maple syrup, as he says something that makes me laugh. This might seem like nothing special. Just two partners, eating pancakes together on a Sunday afternoon. What's remarkable to me though is the complete absence of thoughts or worry about weight and calories. The calorie calculator and militant dictator in my head eventually stopped.

I can walk by a mirror and often the main thought is simply "wow my hair looks wild today." I realize that the way that my body looks is really just NOT important. The level of mental space that has been freed up is honestly mind blowing. I have moments of joy, meaningful connection with friends, a wonderful relationship, and a career and life that I love.

When I was deeply struggling with my eating disorder, I went to a yoga retreat where the instructor asked us to pick a word for how we wanted to feel in the New Year. The word that I chose was "free." I never thought that I'd actually be able to get there one day. And now, freedom feels a MILLION times better than living trapped in my eating disorder (or any of my other self-numbing strategies) ever did.

Alrighty, so now that you've heard about my story, let's shift the focus back to you. I'm here to help. While everyone's path to recovery is going to look a little different, this book is full of tools, tips, and topics that Colleen and I wish we'd had access to in our own recovery.

We want everyone to know what that freedom that we both mentioned is like. We're guessing you might want that too, which is why you're here. Lucky for you, we're here to share everything we've learned and everything we wish we knew. We're going to hit ya with the no-holds-barred version of recovery.

On your marks, get set...go!

Reference

Sorkin, A. (Writer) & Schlamme, T. (Director). (2000, December 13). Noël. [Television series episode]. In A. Sorkin, T. Schlamme, and J. Wells (Producers), *The West Wing*. New York, NBC.

1 Am I Just Dieting?

How to Tell When the Line Has Been Crossed

Before we get into it, let's address something right off the top – something we both get asked about all the time: What is the difference between eating disorders, disordered eating, chronic dieting, and just feeling weird around food?

It's important to acknowledge that disordered eating is a spectrum. At one side you have people who generally feel ok about their bodies but have "food police" thoughts pop up (more on that later), feel a little too loyal to the gym, or go on the occasional diet. On the other side, you have people who have serious medical complications, who can no longer function in their day-to-day lives, and are often in a higher level of care (if it's accessible). And then there are the infinite gradients between the two, where the majority of people fall.

That all being said, where you fall on this spectrum isn't actually that important for the purposes of this book. We're talking to everyone, wherever you are in your journey or your recovery. Maybe you've been in formal treatment centers, maybe you're working with a therapist but still really unsure what recovery will look like for you, maybe you're just sick and tired of counting macros or whatever the diet du jour is and you happened upon this book (yay – by the way). We're talking to all of you. Because the truth is, while all paths to healing are unique, they can have some similar landmarks, regardless of the starting point.

But wait! You may be thinking. *How do I tell if this is even a problem?*

Alright, let's really dig into this. If you're like a lot of our clients you might think you're "just dieting" or you might even realize that you have some weird shit going on with food but "not doing anything that other people aren't doing." And you would be right! But this isn't because it's normal – it's because way more people have disordered relationships with food than we realize. Some estimates show that up to 75% of women have some sort of disordered eating (UNCCH, 2008). Think about that next time you're in a group of women: chances are three out of every four are doing something funky with food. And this makes it really easy to pretend like there's nothing weird about what you're doing because hey, everyone is doing it! Again, this shit isn't normal: it's pervasive.

Now, if you will, put a pin in that for a second so we can talk about dieting in a little more depth. By definition, the word diet just refers to the kinds of food that one eats. But our guess is that's not where your mind first goes when you hear the word. Our guess is you think about all the diets you see in the media and hear about in the break room at work – you know the ones we mean. The current iterations (if you're reading this book around the time it's published; lawd knows what people are doing with food if you're reading this in the future) involve keto, intermittent fasting, paleo, vegan, raw vegan, Whole30, yada yada yada. Fifteen years ago, it was all about low-carb diets and 30 years ago, it was all about low-fat diets. And this goes on and on – in fact, we've done a little research so you can see the diet trends of the last few hundred years.

Ergo, we present to you, a brief history of *DIETING THROUGH THE AGES.*

A diet is not a 19th century phenomenon. We humans have been attempting to control our food intake since the beginning of time – or at least since 3rd century B.C. This is when Hippocrates recommended a diet of light foods, slow running, wrestling, seawater enemas, and vomiting after lunch (RamHormozi, 2019).

Err – what?! Hippocrates was encouraging bulimia? Yes and no. Hippocrates was focused on trying different things to help the human body perform better. Weight was not really the focus here. But regardless – his recommendations show that humans have been focused on manipulating food and our bodies for thousands of years.

However, come 1087 we do find weight to be the focus of at least one diet! William the Conqueror reportedly became too heavy to ride his horse around this time (DeAndrea & Wood, 2017).

He supposedly started a diet of "alcohol only," in order to lose the weight that he had gained, with the hopes of eventually getting back on his horse. (Totally logical right?)

Um…ok William. Seems like a diet that is destined to fail. But most of us can probably identify with his desperation. His focus on alcohol over solid food sends the message "**Lose weight at all costs!**"

Fast forward to 1917, and you will find our very first mention of calories, and the idea that they need to be counted. Dr. Lulu Hunt Peters published the very first best-selling American diet book, "Diet and Health with Key to the Calories" (Smith, 2004).

"*Key to the Calories*" – now we are starting to get into some familiar territory. What follows this book publication is a quick and chaotic slide into the diet-culture mayhem of America.

- 1925: *Lucky Strike cigarette brand launches the "Reach for a Lucky instead of a sweet" campaign.*
- 1930s: *The Grapefruit Diet – AKA the Hollywood Diet – is born. Low-cal plan calls for eating grapefruit with every meal.*

- 1963: *Weight Watchers is founded by Jean Nidetch, a self-described "overweight housewife obsessed with cookies."*
- 1977: *Slim-Fast – a shake for breakfast, a shake for lunch, and then a "sensible" dinner – becomes a diet staple. (PS – what the actual hell?)*
- 1980s: *Aerobics craze steps into high gear when Jane Fonda launches her first exercise video. "No pain, no gain" becomes the new exercise mantra. (*eye roll*)*
- 1985: *Americans go low-fat, eating foods like McDonald's "McLean Deluxe" burger.*
- 1992: *Robert C. Atkins, MD, publishes Dr. Atkins' New Diet Revolution, a high-protein, low-carb plan. (Sound familiar?)*
- 1995: *The Zone Diet, which calls for a specific ratio of carbs, fat, and protein at each meal, begins to attract celeb fans.*
- 2000: *Gwyneth Paltrow – endorses the Macrobiotic Diet, a restrictive Japanese plan based on whole grains and veggies.*
- 2003: *Miami doctor Arthur Agatston, MD, adds fuel to the low-carb craze by publishing* The South Beach Diet. *This is seen as a more moderate version of Atkins.*
- 2011: *Cardiologist Dr. William Davis published* Wheat Belly, *and the gluten-free movement gains momentum. (That book is now the bane of our existence.) (Rotchford, 2013)*
- 2013: *The Paleo Diet – which emphasizes eating like a caveman – takes off. (Barclay, 2013)*
- 2015: *An influx of studies claiming support for the assertion that "sugar is toxic" are released. (Park, 2015)*
- 2019: *Intermittent fasting (known previously by its other name: starvation) takes off. (Healy, 2019)*

Oof. It's been a rough couple of decades. It feels like every food group has been demonized at some point and we didn't even get into all the "niche" diets like the alkaline diet, blood type diet, the military diet, and the baby food diet (gross). There are literally hundreds more that we won't go into but you get the point: there's a *ton* of them and most of them were invented by people who didn't really know what they were doing.

So, while we're at it, let's talk about the term "lifestyle change," shall we? "Lifestyle change" has just become a code word for dieting since more formal dieting fell out of vogue sometime after the 90s. Diet culture has gotten even more slippery in the past decade or so. In the 1960s, 1970s, 1980s, and even the 1990s diets were typically called just this – diets. As previously discussed, the diet du jour changed and morphed over time, but the wording was the same. South Beach *Diet*. Grapefruit *Diet*. Low-fat *Diet*. Sure, there was pressure to lose weight, but at least we knew what we were working with, right?

But *somewhere* along the way, the term "diet" started to get a bad rap. Maybe it is because we, the dieters, started to notice that all diets, from grapefruit fasts to weight watchers, fail eventually (more on that in a minute peeps). But the big shift from basic dieting to sneaky diets-in-disguise really happened in 2013. Sherry Pagoto (University of Massachusetts Medical School) and Bradley Appelhans (Rush University Medical Center) published material in which they urged people to forget about the word diet. They argued that all diets are "equally as good or bad" in helping people fight to lose weight. *Lifestyle*, they argued, is superior to diet in targeting weight.

Boom. Just like that, the (now infamous term) "lifestyle change" was brought into the American vernacular (lucky us, right?) (Pagoto & Appelhans, 2013).

Lifestyle change – the term *does* sound appealing right? Especially in our current culture of "lifestyle experts" and living "holistically" – it's appealing to think we can make a few changes to our lifestyle that will make us healthier (even though what we're really hoping is to be thinner).

Sounds great, but before we all jump onboard the lifestyle change express, let's break this term down a little bit. What are these researchers getting at anyway?

Well, according to the originators of this research, lifestyle change incudes:

- *Dietary counseling (advice and tips on how to control portions, reduce high-calorie foods and navigate restaurants).*
- *Exercise counseling (learning how to set goals, finding ways to target heart rate and exercise often).*
- *Behavioral modification (advice on how to self-monitor, stay motivated and control hunger).*

Controlling portions? Reducing the amount of high-calorie foods eaten? Controlling hunger? Self-motivating to exercise? Um, how is this different from a good ol' fashioned diet again? We call bullshit folks. It seems to us that the main difference between a "lifestyle change" and a diet is semantics. Cue Shakespeare's "a rose by any other name" and all that.

Now – since we've blown the "lifestyle change" thing to smithereens, let's chat about the other major diet in disguise – clean eating.

Clean eating is a term thrown around a lot these days. But truth be told, a simple, *clear* definition of clean eating is hard to find. This is because there is no scientific unanimity on the definition of clean eating (red flag much?).

In one book, *The Complete Idiot's Guide to Clean Eating*, author Diane Welland (2009) states that clean eating is defined as "a lifestyle with an overall focus on sound nutrition, good health, and regular physical activity." She goes on: "Clean eaters enjoy incredible health benefits, like weight loss, reduced risk of chronic illness, and improved strength." However, this definition is one of hundreds of interpretations of this concept. Don't believe us? Take a look at some of the various definitions that US News identified in an article about clean eating:

> When I think of clean eating, I think of Sankofa. The African word and symbol Sankofa translate as 'to go back and take.' The symbol of a bird arching its neck to take an egg from its back symbolizes one taking from the past what is good and bringing it into the present. Clean eating aims to do just that, promoting positive progress in health by reaching back to a time when we ate more wholesome, minimally processed foods.
>
> (Constance Brown-Riggs, MSEd, RD, CDE, author of *The African American Guide to Living Well with Diabetes*)

> Clean eating = eating foods where nothing healthful has been taken away, and nothing harmful has been added.
>
> (Dawn Jackson Blatner, RDN, author of *The Superfood Swap*)

> Clean eating is when I can see all of the ingredients I am eating.
>
> (Jayne Newmark, MS, RDN, owner of Newmark Nutrition, LLC, Phoenix, Arizona)

> To me, clean eating means eating food I know will benefit my health, mind and body. It's not *all* vegetables, whole grains, fruit and lean protein; sometimes it includes a small piece of chocolate or a glass of wine, when I have balanced it out with physical activity. It's a state of mind and a way of life to remain as positive and as proactive as I can about my health as I approach...60.
>
> (Christine Gerbstadt, MD, RD, Author of *The Doctor's Detox Diet: the Ultimate Weight Loss Prescription*)

> Clean eating is focused on reading labels to make sure there are fewer ingredients; but the best clean foods come with only one ingredient – and many have no labels: leafy green vegetables, berries, citrus fruit, tomatoes, nuts, seeds, wheat berries, oats, lentils, chickpeas and more.
>
> (Sharon Palmer, RDN, author of *Plant-Powered for Life*; Johnson, 2015)

Colleen

Clean eating caused one of my major relapses. True story. I fell down the rabbit hole of the "wellness craze" in graduate school and I fell *freakin' hard*. After years of my eating disorder looking like blatant disordered behavior, my desire to be "healthy" looked – well – healthier! I began to find myself more and more concerned about spirulina and raw vegetables but to be honest, this didn't seem so bad! It was only after I began to see that clean eating had become an obsession – that my obsession with weight and emptiness had simply been transferred to an all-consuming obsession with "health" – that I was able to say, "Um yeah. So I'm screwed again. I need help."

We can definitely garner a few commonalities from those definitions of clean eating. First, there is an emphasis on health. Many of the definitions note that clean eating promotes better health. Second, there is an emphasis on ingredients, and, more specifically, limiting the number of ingredients in the food that we are consuming. Notice that none of those definitions involved the word "diet?" That's because most clean eating advocates firmly support the fact that *clean eating is not a diet*. BUT – before you drink the koolade, listen to this: The Mayo Clinic defines clean eating as "in essence a diet – just a way of eating" (Zeratsky, 2020). The bottom line is that if it looks like a diet and acts like a diet…it's probably a diet. And anything that includes restrictions, rules, and wagons to fall off of is most certainly a diet. End. Of. Discussion. *drops mic*

Okay are you still with us? That was a lot of information and if you just stumbled upon this book in your local bookstore, your head might be spinning. You might be wondering what this has to do with anything. You might be wondering why we are so anti-diet. Let us explain.

All of the diets (and all other iterations listed earlier) have one thing in common: *they do not work*. They are destined to fail, regardless of how "compliant" a person is. At best, research shows you have *maybe* a 3–5% chance of sustaining weight loss through dieting – and even if you do, that typically means being trapped in a life of strict portion sizes and food rules – AKA not the life we want for anyone. We are led to believe that we fail diets if we're not able to sustain weight loss but the truth is, diets fail us. They don't work for the large majority of people unless by "work" you mean create disappointment, shame, and body hatred. And this isn't just our opinion – there is plenty of research that shows dieting for weight loss fails in the long term (and very little research that shows it's possible) (Miller, 1999).

The truth is that our bodies have a weight range that they feel most comfortable in where all body systems can function properly, and our bodies are capable of maintaining that weight without much effort on our parts (kind of like homeostasis for our bodies). That's called our *set point* range and it's determined mostly by genetics. In fact, research shows that up to 80% of our body shape and size are determined by genetics, meaning we have *way less control* over the size and shape of our bodies than diet culture would have us believe (Renkl, 2010). But the diet industry would sooner start selling human shit as health food before ever admitting that their products don't actually work. (Oh wait. There actually already is a poop diet. Cool.

Cool.) (Lee, 2016) So, they keep selling their products with slight variations and luring people in with promises they know they can't keep.

We've talked to enough people to know what at least some of you are thinking: *but some people need to be on diets for medical reasons!* And yes, of course this is true. There are certainly people who need to follow specific nutrition parameters to manage a health condition. In the biz, we call this medical nutrition therapy (MNT). MNTs are evidence-based practices that help people manage health concerns. Examples of this may be avoiding gluten if you have Celiac disease, pairing carbohydrates with protein and fiber for better insulin control in diabetics, or eating a low fiber diet if you have Crohn's disease. In fact, the Keto Diet actually is evidenced-based in children with epilepsy (it can help control seizure frequency). All of these things, of course, are valid.

But (and this is a big but!) it is so, so important to see a doctor if you have a medical concern. We CONSTANTLY see clients diagnosing themselves with various intolerances. If you relate, you might as well call yourself Tom Cruise because that is some risky business. We won't get too into the nitty gritty here but it is important to remember that eating disorders and GI (gastrointestinal issues) disorders have a huge overlap so if you're suffering from an eating disorder, chances are you might be experiencing some GI discomfort. At this point, a lot of people think that something they're eating is causing this discomfort but more often than not, it's what they're *not* eating. The more a person restricts/engages in eating disorder behaviors/does wonky things with food, the more their GI system gets confused and the more their microbiome is suppressed. So, barring any medical need (which is why a visit to a doctor is so important friends!), there is no need to restrict anything to make this better. In fact, restriction only perpetuates the problem. The solution, in most cases, is consistent, varied, adequate intake. So, while some diets are medically necessitated and important to follow, what we see far more often is clients diagnosing their own intolerances which can get pretty sticky. If you have a medical condition, by all means please do what you need to do to take care of yourself. But otherwise, tread carefully when it comes to diagnosing intolerances and if you have any concerns, go see the damn doctor.

What we're getting at here (in case you couldn't tell) is that dieting for the intention of weight loss is dangerous and most of the time, fruitless. Because here is the thing: dieting distances us from our body's needs and natural cues. It makes us believe that our body's natural instincts are wrong, that they can't be trusted. It makes us believe that if we're left to our own devices, our bodies would simply be out of control so we need this diet/plan/supplement/workout to stay in control.

But the more someone tries to gain control over their body through tools of diet culture, the more they lose control and silence their body's natural inclination. Very few people are able to stay on diets without starting to feel like their bodies are wrong and that their failed attempts to lose weight are a personal failure. And from there, friends, it's a slippery slope into disordered eating.

What we are getting at here is that the line between dieting and disordered eating can become very, *very* thin, which is why we're not concerned with whether you've been diagnosed with an eating disorder or whether you've been chronically and miserably bouncing from diet to diet for the last few years. If you've ever been on a diet and felt like a failure, then we're talking to you. Because at the end of the day, if you're feeling like your relationship with food is strained or it's causing you more stress than not, then it's worth taking a closer look at and exploring how food can fit into your life in a relaxed, flexible, positive way.

Jennifer

My eating disorder was triggered by many things, but one huge factor that contributed was going on a diet. I had gained weight through binge drinking in college and decided to go on a diet. It started out innocently enough. I bought frozen diet meals and generally ate bland diet-y foods (insert gagging emoji face here). Everyone praised me for losing weight (thanks cultural fatphobia!). There wasn't an exact moment when things shifted from dieting to a full-blown eating disorder, however, eventually I became a shell of my former self. I isolated myself from friends and family, avoided eating out, restricted heavily, and exercised obsessively. I thought about food and my weight 24/7. Here's the thing though – the disordered eating and eventual eating disorder both existed on a continuum and neither was "healthy" for me in any way. So, whether you are struggling with an eating disorder or disordered eating, both are serious and you deserve to get help!

Journaling Prompts

1. If you're unsure whether your relationship with food, exercise, and your body is unhealthy, we've created this quick little litmus test for you. Check yes if you have:
   - Restricted food as a way to lose weight.
   - Cut out food/food groups in the name of health (barring medical necessity).
   - Been following rules about when/what/where/how to eat.
   - Ignored your own hunger in an attempt to control your body.
   - Counted macros, points, calories, or any other external indicator of food consumption.
   - Believed there's only one weight your body can be healthy at.

- Believed that there's only one weight you can be happy at.
- Felt like a failure if you weren't able to get to that weight.
- Felt like you had to compensate for eating through exercise or purging behaviors.
- Felt like you couldn't trust your body.
- Felt like your success as a human is dependent on your weight.

If you checked yes to any of them, then your relationship with food, exercise, or your body has some unhealthy aspects to it.

2. Now take a look at your check marks. Write down:
   a. How each of these dieting behaviors is stealing from the quality of your life right now.
   b. Why you believe challenging this behavior is important for your future.
3. Imagine what a future without food rules could look like. Write about a day, five years from now, when you live food-rule free. What are you doing? Who are you hanging out with? What is up with your thoughts and emotions? What role does food play in your life? It's important to be able to visualize what the hell you are fighting for with all of this!

References

Barclay, E. (2013, December 30). Was 2013 really the year of the paleo diet? NPR. www.npr.org/sections/thesalt/2013/12/27/257669972/was-2013-really-the-year-of-the-paleo-diet?t=1604470302239

DeAndrea, R. & Wood, J. (2017). *7 Simple Rules of Weight Loss*. Bangkok Book Publishing.

Healy, M. (2019, December 5). Eating only during a 10-hour window improved health for those with metabolic syndrome. *Los Angeles Times*. www.latimes.com/science/story/2019-12-05/time-restricted-eating-intermittent-fasting-metabolic-syndrome?hss_channel=tw-18198832

Johnson, M. (2015, March 26). What does clean eating mean to dietitians? US News and World Report. https://wtop.com/news/2015/03/what-does-clean-eating-mean-to-dietitians/

Lee, B. (2016, July 17). Should you eat poop to lose weight? Forbes. www.forbes.com/sites/brucelee/2016/01/17/should-you-eat-poop-to-lose-weight/?sh=56949807766d

Miller, W.C. (1999). How effective are traditional dietary and exercise interventions for weight loss? *Med Sci Sports Exerc.*, Aug; 31(8): 1129–1134.

Pagoto, S. & Appelhans, B. (2013). A call for an end to the diet debates. *JAMA*. 310(7): 687–688.

Park, A. (2015, October 29). Sugar is definitely toxic, a new study says. Time Magazine. https://time.com/4087775/sugar-is-definitely-toxic-a-new-study-says/

RamHormozi, H. (2019). *The Anatomy of Consumerism: The Story of Excess, Greed, Self-Indulgence, Wealth Accumulation, Insurmountable Waste, and Environmental Degradation*. Altona, Manitoba, Canada: Friesen Press.

Renkl, M. (2010). Destined to inherit your mom's body? Women's Health. www.nbcnews.com

Rotchford, L. (2013, February 8). Diets through history: The good, the bad and the scary. CNN Health. https://edition.cnn.com/2013/02/08/health/diets-through-history/index.html

Smith, A.F. (2004). *The Oxford Encyclopedia of Food and Drink in America*, Second Edition. Oxford, England: Oxford University Press.

UNCCH. (2008, April 22). University of North Carolina Chapel Hill Press Release.

Welland, D. (2009). *The Complete Idiot's Guide to Clean Eating*. New York, New York: Alpha Books.

Zeratsky, K. (2020). What is Clean Eating? Mayo Clinic. www.mayoclinic.org/healthy-lifestyle/nutrition-and-healthy-eating/expert-answers/clean-eating/faq-20336262

2 Challenging "Not Sick Enough"

You've seen them. We know you have. The *Glamour* magazine articles about the girls with restrictive eating disorders, complete with pictures of their emaciated bodies. The lifetime movie about the extremely underweight girl with anorexia who has a brush with death and then miraculously *poof* gets her head on straight and recovers from that eating disorder. We know you've seen them because we have *all* seem them. The media *loves* voyeuristic features about individuals with low-weight anorexia diagnoses. And this contributes to a really alarming problem – the problem of all other types and presentations of eating disorders going largely unidentified and untreated. This skewed media coverage also contributes to *so many* people believing that they are "not sick enough" to have an eating disorder.

The fact of the matter is this: being underweight is one symptom of an eating disorder. ONE. And, more importantly, it is a symptom that is not present in the majority of people with eating disorders. That's right! You read that correctly. The majority of folks with eating disorders do not *ever* fall into the underweight category of BMI (side note – BMI is absolute BS; we'll get to that later).

So why does this one symptom of an eating disorder get so much attention? Why is everyone bamboozled into believing that if someone is not visibly the very picture of death, then they are not truly ill?

Well, we would argue that our cultural obsession with weight loss creates a subsequent cultural obsession with low-weight anorexia. Let's be real here – as a society, we are *enamored* with thinness. We romanticize emaciation because we romanticize control. Our harder-better-faster-stronger emphasis creates a glorification of busy, of achievement, and of control. And anorexia is seen as the very embodiment of control (Gard & Freeman, 1996).

We're not just ranting here. The proof is in the pudding. The vast majority of eating disorder research is focused on low-weight anorexia. The majority of inpatient eating disorder admissions have anorexia. The majority of managed care plans mandate that an individual must have a low body weight in order to receive coverage. The entire eating disorders treatment model has been swept away in anorexia-fascination. And it is *not* ok (Mulders-Jones & Mitchison, 2017).

What about people who struggle with restriction who never lose weight? What about those who struggle with restriction while living in a larger body size? What about the people who experience bingeing, purging, or laxative abuse as their main eating disorder symptom? What about the folks who struggle with compulsively exercising who appear to be "fit" (whatever the hell that means), but not emaciated? What about those who never lose their periods? What about those who never lose any weight, yet fall into the trap of becoming obsessed with food in the name of "health"?

We're here to say, for the record, that anyone who falls into any of those categories is sick. Yes, even if you do not have a diagnosed eating disorder. And by the way, can we take a second to rant about the diagnosis system for eating disorders? Because it is, excuse our French here, sort of *f*cked.*

Colleen

Hot take – I was actually *more* miserable and depressed (and arguably "sicker") in my eating disorder when I was not underweight. That's right. Don't get me wrong – the times when I lost a ton of weight sucked. Truly they did. But people were concerned. They asked if I was ok. Doctors were kind and caring. Put plainly, others noticed that I needed a life boat and so they rowed out to get me. But I found that during the times that I was weight-restored, and struggling *just as much* mentally and emotionally – well, during those times I was more on my own. Most didn't even think to throw me a life jacket. It felt like if I didn't wear the fact that I was drowning on my body, then nobody cared or knew. It felt like being underweight was the only way that "sick enough" was in reach. This is bullshit because I was sick regardless of what weight I was. This is why, these days, I am a HUGE advocate for my clients being "sick enough." I am constantly reminding people of this: Are you feeling distressed about your relationship with food and your body? Cool. You are sick enough. I don't give a rat's ass about you not being "underweight" by BMI standards. You are sick. You are also enough. End o' story.

EATING DISORDER DIAGNOSIS RANT: Currently, in the biz, we use the Diagnostic and Statistical Manual of Mental Disorders-5 (DSM-5) to diagnose eating disorders. This manual separates out the diagnoses into anorexia, bulimia, binge eating disorder, and avoidant and restrictive food intake disorder. The classification system mandates that folks meet certain criteria in order to qualify for a diagnosis of each specific eating disorder.

So, let's talk about anorexia. For a diagnosis of anorexia, someone must display all of these qualities:

A)   Persistent restriction of energy intake leading to significantly low body weight (in context of what is minimally expected for age, sex, developmental trajectory, and physical health).

B)   Either an intense fear of gaining weight or of becoming fat, or persistent behavior that interferes with weight gain (even though one is a significantly low weight).

C)   Disturbance in the way one's body weight or shape is experienced, undue influence of body shape and weight on self-evaluation, or persistent lack of recognition of the seriousness of the current low body weight.

(American Psychiatric Association, 2013)

For a diagnosis of bulimia, on the other hand, one must exhibit the following:

A)   Recurrent episodes of binge eating.

B)   Recurrent compensatory behavior (i.e. vomiting, laxatives, diuretics, fasting or excessive exercise).

C)   The binge eating and compensatory behaviors both occur, on average, at least once a week for three months.

D)   Self-evaluation is unduly influenced by body shape and weight.

(American Psychiatric Association, 2013)

For a diagnosis of binge eating disorder, the criteria are:

A)   Recurrent episodes of binge eating.

B)   Binge eating occurs, on average, at least once a week for three months.

(American Psychiatric Association, 2013)

For a diagnosis of avoidant and restrictive food intake disorder (note: this is a newer eating disorder that was identified in the past few years), the criteria are as follows:

A)   Persistent failure to meet appropriate nutritional and/or energy needs associated with one (or more) of the following:
1. Significant loss of weight (or failure to achieve expected weight gain or faltering growth in children).
2. Significant nutritional deficiency.
3. Dependence on enteral feeding or oral nutritional supplements.
4. Marked interference with psychosocial functioning.

B)   There is no evidence of a disturbance in the way one's body weight or shape is experienced.

(American Psychiatric Association, 2013)

Why are we laying this out for you? To show you how narrow and arbitrary these categories actually are. For example, when it comes to the anorexia diagnosis, what does "significantly low body weight" really mean? Human beings come in all shapes and sizes. What is significantly low for one person might be the natural size for another. What does significantly low look like when someone is simply supposed to exist in a larger body?

This type of criteria is sort of nonsensical and subjective when you break it down. Research shows that people who exhibit all the other traits of anorexia *except for the low body weight* have the *same* medical and psychiatric complications as those who meet the full criteria (Golden & Mehler, 2020).

And what about bulimia? Is the psychological impact of bingeing and purging once every week and a half much less than the impact of bingeing and purging once a week? Why the black and white cut off points?

The DSM-5 tries to address the issue with the category, "other specified feeding and eating disorder" (otherwise known as OSFED), which is basically their "catch-all" eating disorder diagnosis. It's a diagnosis that says, "you have some symptoms of one eating disorder, and maybe other symptoms of another – but you don't technically fit into any of our boxes."

The thing is, OSFED is one of the most common eating disorder diagnoses. Which raises the point: if one of the most common eating disorder diagnoses is the diagnosis where people don't fit into any of the diagnoses, maybe the entire system needs an overhaul? (This is not rocket science people.)

The good news is, the field is moving more and more towards a continuum model for talking about eating disorders – meaning that, in the future ('sup DSM-6?) there might just be one umbrella eating disorder diagnosis, which would be, in our humble opinion, *so much freaking better.*

SO – the point of our DSM rant, especially in the context of this "sick enough" chapter, is that the eating disorder diagnoses are not the end all when it comes to understanding if you do, in fact, have a problem. In fact, for the duration of this book, when we use the term "eating disorder" please know that we are referring to: *disordered eating that gets in the way of your quality of life. Diagnosis or not.*

END DIAGNOSIS RANT

If you have ever found yourself thinking "*I'm not sick enough,*" take comfort in the fact that you are not alone in this thought. We can honestly say that we have never met anyone who has suffered from an eating disorder that has not had this thought. But next time you find yourself thinking this, remember: this thought itself suggests that you are, in fact, "sick enough," because this is a pretty sick thought to have. After all, healthy people do not tend to wish to be ill.

The most telling factor for any mental health issue is this: does it have a negative impact on your social, emotional, *or* physical functioning? So, there you have it – the only answer you need to answer the "not sick enough" conundrum: Is your life being negatively impacted by your relationship with food and/or your body? If the answer is yes (and, if you are reading this book, we are 99.9% sure it is), then congratulations – you are sick enough.

Jennifer

Oh man. The "not sick enough" struggle is something that I experienced A LOT in recovery. I didn't fit the vision of what I thought someone with an eating disorder "looked like." I had lost a significant amount of weight in my eating disorder – but because I didn't appear emaciated, people didn't seem too concerned about me. Early on, I remember telling a friend that I thought I might have a problem and she was like, "You don't look too thin, you look great!" Later on, my eating disorder loved to tell me that I wasn't "that sick" as a way to keep me stuck. Eventually, I had to challenge that belief because I was really miserable. Educating myself more on eating disorders and how they truly "don't have a look" – plus consistently talking back to the voice in my head – definitely helped. It was also important for me to continue to work on recovery even in times when my mind was telling me that I "wasn't that sick." So let me shout this from the rooftop for a moment – no matter what you weigh you ARE 100 PERCENT SICK ENOUGH.

The desire to be sick is, in and of itself, a disordered thought, and one that stems directly back to the biological and chemical roots of disordered eating itself. Research conducted among samples of people who display disordered eating demonstrates unusually high levels of altered response to pain, emotion intensity, hunger and satiety, and assessment of body shape/body image. This suggests that part of the brain that senses pain related to physical and psychological experiences does not function properly (which may, in part, account for the "numbing effect" that many people with eating disorders report). So, an individual suffering from an eating disorder may be physically or psychologically compromised, but their brain *does not sense this*. As a result, they can actually be quite ill but their brain (and specifically the disordered eating part of their brain chemistry) is still feeding them thoughts of "not sick enough" (Alkazemi et al., 2018; Wagner et al., 2015).

To put it plainly – you will never be sick enough, because there *is no* sick enough. The sick enough that you are chasing is a disappearing goal post, a mirage. We've had frank conversations with the very people who could star on those eating disorder lifetime movies – people who have had the NG tube/those who have been to treatment x amount of times, etc., and guess what? They all reiterate the very same thought:

"I just never saw myself as sick enough."

This is why, when the "not sick enough" thought comes to mind, it is important to consciously process and acknowledge the fact that this is *your eating disorder speaking*. That's right. This is the eating disorder getting very crafty – the eating disorder whispers "Not sick enough," and you find yourself moving more and more towards the eating disorder.

If you want recovery, you *must* challenge this thought immediately. Ask yourself, "What does sick enough mean? And why do I want to be sick? What will I get out of being sick enough? What will I achieve from being the sickest?"

Challenge your eating disorder voice on this every. single. time. *Do not* let your eating disorder voice bully you into thinking that being sick = happiness.

So: A quick reminder that your eating disorder is a real and valid experience even if...

- You have never been underweight.
- You have never been inpatient.
- You are weight-restored.
- Your labs look fine.
- You have never been on an NG tube/never drank Ensure/never been near death.
- You've been told you don't "look like" you have an eating disorder.
- You've never been to a therapist.
- You don't have a strikingly alarming "rock bottom story" about your eating disorder.
- You don't restrict food groups/count calories.
- You don't feel triggered by the media or diet culture.
- Your friends or family don't know.
- Your friends or family don't believe you.
- You like to eat certain things/look forward to meals.
- You don't fear foods.
- You don't fear foods that others seem to.
- You don't use the behaviors that people most commonly speak about when they discuss eating disorders.
- You don't exercise.
- Your recovery is going smoothly.
- Your journey/gender/ethnicity/identity does not match the most common portrayal of eating disorders in the media or the memoirs.

Summarily – ban/obliterate/kick out "not sick enough." Argue relentlessly with this thought when it springs to mind. You are sick. You are also enough. The relationship ends there.

Quiz: How to tell if you are "sick enough."

1) Is your relationship with food and/or your body negatively impacting your quality of life?
Yes – You are "sick enough."
No – awesome. Keep livin' your life.

Journaling Prompt

1. What does your eating disorder try to convince you that "sick enough" is?
2. Where might this idea stem from?
3. Write out a dialogue between your eating disorder and yourself about this. Your eating disorder's job in this dialogue is to explain to you just what "sick enough" means, and your job is to explain back why this is absolute horseshit.

References

Alkazemi, D., Zafar, T., Ebrahim, M., & Kubow, S. (2018). Distorted weight perception correlates with disordered eating attitudes in Kuwaiti College Women. *International Journal of Eating Disorders*, 51(5): 449–458.

American Psychiatric Association (2013). *Diagnostic and Statistical Manual of Mental Disorders: Diagnostic and Statistical Manual of Mental Disorders*, Fifth Edition. Arlington, VA: American Psychiatric Association.

Gard, M. & Freeman, C. (1996). The dismantling of a myth: a review of eating disorders and socioeconomic status. *International Journal of Eating Disorders*, 20(1): 1–12.

Golden, N. & Mehler, P. (2020). Atypical anorexia can be just as bad. *Cleveland Clinic Journal of Medicine*, 87(3): 172–174.

Mulders-Jones, B. & Mitchison, D. (2017). Socioeconomic correlates of eating disorder symptoms in an Australian population-based sample. *PLoS ONE* 12(1).

Wagner, A., Simmons, A.N., Tyson, A.O., Guido, F., McCurdy-McKinnon, D., Fudge, J., Yang, T., Paulas, M., & Kayne, W. (2015). Altered sensitization patterns to sweet food stimuli in patients recovered from anorexia and bulimia nervosa. *Psychiatry Res.* Dec 30, 234(3): 305–313.

3   Early Recovery
Changing Your Behaviors

So, you're here. You've picked up this book. You've read chapters one and two and have decided "Yeah, I do have a problem. And hell yeah. I am sick enough." Can we just take a minute to give you a major metaphorical fist bump for getting to *this* point in your journey? Realizing that you have a problem and deciding to change is no small feat. So, go you! Celebrate yourself – you are well on your way to kicking some eating disorder booty.

The next step is to take a step. That's right – you're gonna have to actually do it – change some of the ways that you interact with food and your body. Essentially, you're going to have to begin to change your behaviors. This will arguably be one of the toughest parts of this journey, but it is an *imperative* step – especially when you are in early recovery. There's no way around it. We can teach you all about how the thoughts you are having about your body stem back to our messed-up culture. You can trace your feelings around food back to the messages that you absorbed via your fam throughout childhood. But at the end of the day, *nothing changes if nothing changes.* This is super important to understand. Nothing changes if you do not change your behavior. The tough pill to swallow here is that you most likely will have to "act as if."

"Acting as if" means behaving in a specific way *as if* you truly feel in accordance with that behavior. In other words, it means doing the damn thing, even if you don't feel like it. Examples of acting as if could be:

1. Giving a speech and attempting to convey confidence, even though you are internally peeing yourself.
2. Showing up to a friend's birthday party and smiling/being social, even though you are having a bad day and really wanted to stay in bed.
3. Asking for a raise in an assertive manner, even when you may not "truly believe" that you are worthy.

We're gonna give it to you straight here. Acting as if is not pleasant. Look at those examples – they all involve some level of discomfort. That's because acting as if requires you to do something that might go against your internal instincts. For example, giving a speech can feel really terrifying. If you are anything like us, your heart might race before a speech. Your palms may feel sweaty. Your mind might be screaming "RUN!" Everything in your body is sending you signals *not* to give the speech. BUT – and here is the MOST IMPORTANT "but" to remember – these signals are actually not accurate. You may feel physically uncomfortable. You may think, "I will literally die if I have to get up in front of those people." But the thought is not accurate. It's not fact. The emotions and physical sensations are not truly fitting for what is actually happening.

Why? Who really knows? *shrug* Human beings do this. We get our signals crossed in life sometimes. We associate innocuous situations with danger incorrectly. Maybe we saw our parents freak out before a public speaking gig. Maybe we drank too much coffee one day and our heart started racing prior to giving a presentation. Whatever the origin, physical and psychological signals got crossed, and our brain is now sending us "flee" signals. (This is how phobias are formed.) It sucks. But it's fixable people. That's right – you can uncross those weird signals – you'll just have to push past some certain discomfort to do so. That's when "acting as if" comes in.

Colleen

I honestly felt that "acting as if" was one of the WORST parts of recovery. Lawd did I hate this part. My clients seem to agree with this sentiment. It's a tough spot to be in because you are being asked to change your behaviors, which is SO hard, and you are likely not going to see the psychological benefits from doing so right away. The only thing I can tell you is to push through. Trust that what we are telling you is true. Trust this process. Trust that this beginning part is hard – that this recovery jam might actually hurt MORE than the eating disorder at the beginning. This is because recovery is like frostbite. It hurts more as it heals. But nobody ever got better from frostbite by running back into the blizzard. You hear me? Keep. Going.

"Acting as if" often means doing something courageous WHILE feeling terrified. The good news here is that the more you *do it afraid*, the easier things get over time. The more you give speeches, the less scary they feel. It is research proven. Essentially, the more you "act as if," the less acting you will have to do over time.

Can you list out your own examples of "acting as if" that you can recall from your past?

1. ....
2. ....
3. ....

In order to recover from an eating disorder, a lot of "acting as if" around food has to happen early on. For this reason, we are going to pull from a type of therapy called CBT. CBT stands for cognitive behavior therapy. CBT is a type of therapy that focuses on the links between our emotions, thoughts, and behaviors. It focuses on changing your thoughts and behaviors to positively impact your emotions and ultimately change your whole life. You might be interested to know that CBT is one of the few empirically-based techniques that has been shown to successfully reduce eating disorder symptomology (translation: it's been shown to help a lot of people kick their eating disorders' asses) (Fairburn, 2008).

CBT stresses the importance of learning the skills, and implementing them to create actual changes in your behavior. Implementing the skills is where the "acting as if" comes in. For example, if you freak out about eating carbs, part of your process is going to involve "acting as if" you are cool with eating all the carbs. Acting as if you can turn your eating disorder voice down. Essentially, you're going to have to eat the carbs, and breathe through the fear and discomfort that comes up.

In fact, we want to urge you to commit to taking one new "acting as if" step each week as you read through this book. The steps can be teeny tiny. Gradual is cool. As long as you are slowly but surely taking the teeny tiny "acting as if" steps – you got this. The thing to remember here is that the discomfort that comes up for you at first, as you are making these changes, recedes over time. It won't feel like it. Your eating disorder voice will tell you that the discomfort will last forever, but remember – that voice is horse-shit. Can't trust it, we tell ya.

Jennnifer

I remember when I first met with an eating disorder dietitian and she asked that I add in more food to what I was currently eating – including dessert. I was scared but there was also some exhilaration as I shopped at Trader Joes for desserts. I went through a one- or two-week honeymoon period where I wondered "was I even struggling with an eating disorder?" In hindsight, the food felt easier to add in at that point because I knew that I needed to gain weight and because a professional had just "given me permission." However, once I started gaining weight, I found that challenging my eating disorder was sooooo much harder. I was so terrified at that point that challenging all of my rigid rules around food felt so freaking tough. But I noticed that the more that I challenged a specific fear food, the easier it became to eat that food over time. The more that you challenge your eating disorder rules, the easier it will get as time passes. The discomfort that you are feeling is completely TEMPORARY so keep pushing forward even on the days when you feel like giving up. It will be so worth it when you are finally free.

So, first thing's first. In order to change a behavior, you first need to know what the behavior actually is. There are many different ways to experience disordered eating and negative body image, so we will outline a few of the most common for you here. Put a check mark next to the behaviors that you find yourself commonly doing:

1. Cutting out food groups (for non-medical reasons).
2. Restricting volume of food (not allowing yourself to eat enough).
3. Obsessively tracking macros, calories, or other numerical ways of measuring intake.
4. Eating foods, but feeling extreme guilt afterwards (telling yourself that certain foods are "bad").
5. Chewing food and then spitting it out.
6. Purging (throwing up food).
7. Bingeing (eating a large volume of food very quickly, and feeling out of control when doing so).
8. Attempting to control weight/intake via laxatives, diet pills, or similar types of interventions.
9. Exercising because you feel like you "have to."
10. Exercising past the point that your body wants (i.e. even when you're sick, tired, or simply burnt out).
11. Exercising in order to "burn off" food, or with the sole purpose of losing weight.
12. Avoiding eating in front of people.
13. Actively putting down your body to yourself.
14. Body checking (pulling, pinching, or frequently looking in mirrors to examine "flaws").
15. Forgoing activities because you feel scared to show your body.
16. Weight suppressing (actively keeping your weight at a lower point than your body wants it to be *PLEASE NOTE: THIS DOES NOT HAVE TO MEAN YOU ARE "UNDERWEIGHT"*).

Ok. Did you put your check marks in? Good. Because those are some of the most common manifestations of eating disorders. And it's important to identify if you are partaking in any of them If you are doing *any* of those things, some serious behavior changes are going to be necessary.

But before we jump into deciding what to change and how, let's pause for a hot sec to talk about the *why* of the behaviors. Why are you restricting your food to the point of feeling like crap every day? Why are you hating on your bod? Well, if you're anything like us (and the hundreds of clients that we have treated), there is likely no simple answer to that question. We have never met anyone who is able to say, "this single event happened in my life, and THAT is 100% the reason that I now have an eating disorder." For most of us, eating disorders develop as a result of a perfect storm – that is, a coming together of genes, personality, environment, and culture. To explain this better, we'll refer you to what is known in research land as the biopsychosocial model.

The Biopsychosocial Model

The biopsychosocial model is a model for understanding health that includes biological, psychological, and social factors. It's a model that we use to explain mental illness. Essentially, mental illness develops as a result of both genetic/neurochemical factors (bio), personality/mood factors (psycho), and environmental/cultural factors (social). So, to simplify this (admittedly boring) model, we like to use the metaphor of an "eating disorder egg" (Borrell-Carrió et al., 2004).

If you are with us, in the camp of people who have developed an eating disorder (or disordered eating, or a very troubled relationship with food and your body, etc.), then you have, what we like to call, an eating disorder egg in ya. This egg is made up of your genes. Genes lay the foundation for your eating disorder – you can't really develop an eating disorder without that genetic predisposition. Researchers haven't been able to pin down the exact gene combinations yet, but they have discovered some commonalities when it comes to genes of those with eating disorders. A good way to tell if someone has the genes is to look at family; a family history of mental health issues – any mental health issues – increases the odds of having an eating disorder gene set.

SO, if you have those genes, then you have the eating disorder egg. The next part of the equation is that personality/mood starts knock-knock-knockin' on that egg. In other words, there are certain personality factors that can bring these genes out, so to speak. Like sensitivity. Perfectionism. Introversion. Low self-esteem. A tendency towards pessimism or sadness. Impulsivity. Curiosity. Harm avoidance. A tendency towards anxiety. All of these things have been shown to knock on that gene egg. THEN, the third part of the equation is environment. That is, specific variables in our environment can start knockin' on the egg too. This stuff can be cultural – we live in a thin-obsessed dieting culture. It can be trauma – a parent can die, your best friend can suddenly move away, a sexual assault can occur. It can be oppression – maybe you are living in a fat body in a fat-phobic society. Maybe you are a person of color who lives in a society where Eurocentric standards of beauty are thrown at you from every which way. It can be stage of life – hitting puberty early (hi, hello, that's me (Colleen)). It can be bullying. It can be starting a sport. It can be school pressure. It can be peer pressure. Any host of environmental factors can knock on that egg. At some point, after enough knocks, that damn egg CRACKS – enter: eating disorder.

The main take away point here is that the *why* behind your eating and body image is going to be completely unique to you. And as you are moving forward and changing behaviors (you know, "acting as if"), it's going to be super helpful for you to understand your own personal "why." So, give it a try. Fill in the egg outline in Figure 3.1 with your own biopsychosocial stuff.

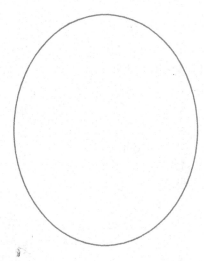

Figure 3.1 Biopsychosocial egg

Now! Back to those pesky behaviors.

Identify the exact behaviors around food, exercise, and your body that cause you distress. Do you restrict snacks? Do you exercise every day? Do you tell yourself that dessert is off limits? Do you weigh yourself often? Write out a list of at least ten behaviors for yourself. This is going to be the list that you base your "acting as if" off of.

1.
2.
3.
4.
5.
6.
7.
8.
9.
10.

Do you have it? Good, because now we want you to write down the pros to keeping the behaviors. Go ahead. Write down all of the reasons why you do not want to change them.

Next, write down the pros to changing the behavior.

•

·

Reflect on the two lists. Which one has more pros? Are some of the pros "weightier" than others? (This means some of them hold more importance to you.) What if we told you that we are *positive* that the pros of changing outweigh the pros of staying the same? Because that's what we are – 100% sure that changing is the better bet. Speaking of bets, we're so sure that we would be willing to bet *our pets* on the fact that changing trumps staying the same. We are sure because all of our research, clinical work, and personal experiences have shown us that healing eating disordered behaviors leads to a more peaceful, fulfilling life. We have NEVER met one person that regrets recovering from an eating disorder. Not One. Single. Person. The pros of changing outweigh the pros of staying the same. We are certain.

Ok! Next step – pick one behavior that you are willing to challenge. One small way that you are willing to start making a change. Some examples of this would be: buying full fat yogurt instead of nonfat. Reducing the number of days that you are working out by one day. Purchasing one package of whatever food your eating disorder has been calling "off limits" and selecting one night this week to eat it.

My first small behavior change will be:………………………………………

These small behavior changes may feel big at first – and that's ok. Your heart may race when you eat that full fat yogurt for the first time. We're asking you to b r e a t h e – and keep eating. B r e a t h e – and stay in bed on that off-exercise day. B r e a t h e – and eat the bagel. B r e a t h e – and sit with the urge to binge or purge. Remind yourself that this "acting as if" step is a step towards your badass life in color.

B r e a t h e . B r e a t h e . B r e a t h e .

Feel the fear, and eat it anyway. After you take your first "acting as if" step, we want you to turn towards one of your tried and true coping skills. This could mean calling a friend for support. This could mean turning on the tv to distract yourself. It could be journaling, taking

a slow mindful walk, doing the dishes – hell it could be more b r e a
t h i n g!

Each time you do this – each time you breathe through "acting as
if" – you are proving something VERY important to yourself. You
are proving that yes you can do this. Yes, you can disobey that eating
disorder voice. It may be scary. It may feel terrible at first. AND you
can do it. You don't die. The world keeps on spinning. Your life keeps
on going. And every time you prove this to yourself, you chip away at
this eating disorder more and more. Which is badass as hell.

Journaling Prompts

1. "Acting as if" might require a lot of distraction – and that's ok! Your
   job right now is to push through and eat anyway – to push through
   and ignore the pull to use a behavior. This means distraction from all
   the tough feelings that are going to come up will be necessary. Journal
   about all the different types of distractions that you can use when the
   bad feelings come a 'knockin'.
2. Next, create a specific distraction list of "competing behaviors." These
   are distractions that make it nearly impossible to engage with your
   eating disorder when you are using them. For example, painting your
   nails, hopping on a skype/facetime call with a friend, or playing catch
   with your dog.

References

Borrell-Carrió, F., Suchman, A., & Epstein, R. (2004). The biopsychosocial model
25 years later: principles, practice, and scientific inquiry. *Annals of Family
Medicine*, 2(6): 576–582.

Fairburn, C. (2008). *Cognitive Behavior Therapy and Eating Disorders*. New York:
Guilford Press.

4 Changing Your Thoughts
Legalize It – Food, That Is!

Alright, so let's be real here. Those pesky eating disorder thoughts have ya feeling pretty anxious and guilty around food, don't they? In this chapter, we're going to help you squash that shit, and legalize it! (Food that is...) Buckle up for some nutrition myth busting.

Let's be real here: broccoli isn't coming to save you and donuts aren't wearing devil horns. Despite what diet culture might lead you to believe – ALL foods can fit into a healthy diet (barring genuine medical restrictions).

You Don't Need to Fear Calories

Let's chat for a minute about calories, shall we? Diet culture has totally demonized them, and your eating disorder may have as well. So what the heck is a calorie anyway?

Well, technically speaking, a calorie "is the amount of heat required to raise the temperature of 1 gram of water by 1 degree Celcius" (Scott, 2019). TRUTH BOMB: we need calories to do everything that we do in our lives. A calorie is a unit of energy. Energy that allows us to dance, walk, laugh, hug the people that we love, talk, and sing. Here is one of our favorite cognitive reframes about this topic: low calorie = less energy to live your best life. (AKA: why you truly do NOT need to fear calories because they are life-giving energy.)

Mantras for Calorie Related Fears

Use this space to write down some mantras that you can tell yourself if your eating disorder starts yelling about calories.

ALL Foods Fit

ALL foods truly can fit into a healthy diet (barring genuine medical restrictions) no matter what your eating disorder or diet culture might say. Anything in extreme quantities can be harmful – however, it's all about dosage and context. If all you ate was donuts every day you would become unhealthy. If all you ate was carrots every day you'd also become unhealthy. Even things like water, the sun, and kale can be harmful in extreme dosages.

For instance, if you drink an extreme amount of water, you can develop hyperhydration which can be deadly (Semeco, 2020). If you spend way too much time in the sun you can get sun poisoning (Robinson, 2018). If you eat a huge amount of kale you can develop thallium poisoning (Lawrence, 2016). The takeaway here is that no one specific food (or food group! We're looking at you low-carb fear mongerers!) is "healthy" or "unhealthy." The aim is to eat a wide variety of foods.

Now – something that's really important to remember here is that *context matters*. The "healthy" choice for *you* is also completely individualized. For instance, if you have anxiety around eating a bag of chips and find yourself hungry for a snack, the HEALTHIEST thing in that moment would be eating the bag of chips because, 1) chips are enjoyable (shoutout to Doritios!) and 2) working on decreasing your anxiety is a healthy choice (because anxiety spikes the stress hormone cortisol and ain't nobody got time for that (Bergland, 2013)). Plus, the chips have carbs and fat which will help to fuel you for your afternoon.

So be aware: the context of our choices is important. Making statements about any particular foods as being "healthy" or "unhealthy" is totally black and white and ignores our individual needs, bodies, gut microbiome, psychology, enjoyment, and overall context of the situation.

All About Those Macronutrients Though

Carbs, fat, and protein – AKA the whole gang of macronutrients – can sometimes be demonized in the media (and by your eating disorder). So, we're gonna break down the importance and the benefits of these macronutrients for you:

Carbs

Oh carbs, we love you (we used to fear you). But diet culture is totally demonizing you. Diet culture and eating disorders *love* to fear-monger around carbohydrates – which is ironic because they're awesome and have a lot of important physical and mental health benefits (Mayo Clinic Staff, 2020).

1 Source of Energy For the Brain + Body

Carbohydrates are the macronutrient that our body needs in the LARGEST amounts (take that keto!). Dietary Guidelines for Americans state that 45–65% of our daily intake should come from carbohydrates (Mayo Clinic Staff, 2020). Carbs are the main fuel source for the body, as they are most easily converted into glucose. Glucose fuels all human activities and is needed for energy (Mayo Clinic Staff, 2020). Beth Rosen, MS, RD, CDN, says, "Carbohydrates contain essential nutrients that our bodies need to function each day. In fact, our brain's nutrient of choice is glucose which comes from carbohydrate intake" (Rollin, 2016a).

So, if you want to have all that good brain power and energy to fuel your life, it's important not to skimp on carbs!

Mood Boosting

Shhhh. There's a secret that the low-carb evangelists don't want you to know about:

Carbohydrates are *important* in terms of mood. And not eating enough of them can have a negative impact on your mental and physical health.

"Carbs are needed to make serotonin, our hormone that helps us feel calm and relaxed, like our own natural 'chill pill'. If you like being in a good mood, make sure carbs are on your menu," says Rebecca Scritchfield, RDN, author of *Body Kindness* (Rollin, 2016a).

This helps to explain why people on low-carb diets can struggle with poor mood and irritability.

Michelle Kuster, RD, LD, explains,

> There's always a nutritional demon; carbs are currently the culprit. With a $60 billion diet industry, marketers think of creative ways to make people fear food. But carbohydrates are your bodies and brain's preferred source of fuel, and even a short time without them will lead to fatigue, headaches and irritability.
>
> (Rollin, 2016a)

Add Pleasure to the Eating Experience

Bagels, pizza, pasta…need we say more?!

While some of these foods might feel scary to your eating disorder (and felt scary to us when we were struggling), they can ultimately add pleasure and satisfaction to the eating experience. Food isn't just about fuel. Yes, carbs provide fuel for the body – however, the eating experience is also about pleasure, satisfaction, and joy.

"Without carbs, meals tend to be less satisfying. Having a source of carbs with meals helps you stay full and happy for longer" says, Josée Sovinsky, RD (Rollin, 2016a).

Even if your eating disorder tells you otherwise, you deserve to nourish your body, feel satisfied, and experience a sense of pleasure from food.

So what happens (aside from low energy, irritability, fatigue, poor mood, etc.) when you restrict carbs? Welp – we'll just cut to the chase here: restricting carbs can lead to a disordered relationship with food and can trigger (or perpetuate) eating disorders in genetically vulnerable individuals.

Christy Harrison, MPH, RD, CDN, registered dietitian nutritionist, certified intuitive eating counselor, and host of *Food Psych* podcast, explains:

> Cutting out carbs is a great way to make yourself start bingeing on them. Because carbs are your body's primary fuel source, your brain is wired to seek them out if there's a shortage. Carbs are essential for keeping your blood sugar from dropping too low. If that happens (as it often does in a low-carb diet), your brain will actually send out neurotransmitters that drive you toward whatever high-carb foods are available. So, people who attempt to cut carbs end up feeling out-of-control around those very foods, without realizing that this is actually their body's way of protecting them. To avoid this vicious cycle of restricting and bingeing on carbs, don't cut them out—instead, learn to trust your body around all foods.
>
> (Rollin, 2016a)

Michelle Kuster, RD, LD, says,

> Any time we over-emphasize one aspect of nutrition, we lose the big picture, which is that all foods can be enjoyed in a balanced diet, and avoiding foods typically leads to unintended consequences such as intrusive or obsessive thoughts about food.
>
> (Rollin, 2016a)

Fat

The media has demonized fat since the 80s when the low-fat diet craze began and people began switching to "fat free" everything. However, the reality is that fat is actually an ESSENTIAL nutrient and your bod needs it for a lot of important functions (Pasquale, 2009). That's right people – turns out, fat is very important (despite what your eating disorder might say!).

The following are just a few of the things that dietary fat does for you:

- Protects your organs.
- Aids with temperature regulation.
- Assists with cell growth.
- Gives your bod energy.
- Hair/skin/nail growth.

(American Heart Association, n.d.)

Robyn Goldberg, RDN, CEDRD, discusses other benefits of having enough fat in your diet when she says, "Eating fat is necessary for temperature regulation. Eating dietary fat will provide our body with healthy hair, skin, and nails. One client said to me, that her hair doesn't look like the scarecrow anymore" (Rollin, 2016b).

Fat plays an important function when it comes to absorbing certain nutrients. Eating fat alongside vegetables, for instance, helps your bod to absorb some of the nutrients that you would not get otherwise (Warner, 2004).

Rachel Wallace Hartley, RD, LD, CDE, explains, "Dietary fat plays critical biological roles in our body including the formation of neurotransmitters, hormones and allowing our body to absorb the fat soluble vitamins A, D, E and K" (Rollin, 2016b).

Lindsay Krasna, RD, CDN, says,

> I always like reminding clients that *all* dietary fats help enhance the body's ability to absorb fat soluble vitamins. So, you can get much more nutritional bang for your buck by eating say carrots with avocado, as opposed to eating the carrots alone.
>
> (Rollin, 2016b)

Turns out you need fat in order to truly reap the nutritional benefit of certain foods. Whatchu know about that, diet culture? And, despite what your eating disorder might say, being able to feel full and satisfied is an important part of the eating experience (and getting enough fat can help with this!). Rachel Wallace Hartley, RD, LD, CDE, explains:

> Fat helps keep you satiated since it digests more slowly. Perhaps most importantly, fat makes food taste delicious, making nutrient dense foods palatable and exciting to eat. Consider carrots slowly roasted and caramelized in olive oil versus plain carrot sticks, rich and creamy full fat yogurt versus fat free, or a salad drizzled with a bright and fresh dressing versus plain lettuce,
>
> (Rollin, 2016b)

Emily Fonnesbeck, RD, says, "Fats provide flavor and satisfaction in a meal, allowing us to leave the table without feeling preoccupied with food" (Rollin, 2016b).

If you want to boost your brain-power and enhance your mood, it's vitally important that you are getting enough fat in your diet. Marci Evans, MS, CEDRD, LDN says,

> Getting enough fat in your diet is correlated with lower rates of anxiety and depression. Your brain is about 60% fat and eating enough of it is critical for your brain to work optimally. When you get enough fat at a meal it signals your gut to tell your brain to relax and that you're

satisfied. This helps you think about food less so you can pay attention to other things.

(Rollin, 2016b)

Emily Fonnesbeck, RD, says,

Dietary fats are essential building blocks for hormones and neurotransmitters. In fact, they play vital roles in brain function, particularly for learning and memory. While there is a lot of discussion about good vs. bad fats, ALL fats have a role in these metabolic functions.

(Rollin, 2016b)

Protein

Protein is found in muscle, skin, bone, hair, and in practically every tissue and body part. It creates the hemoglobin which carries oxygen to your body, as well as the enzymes which power lots of chemical reactions. (Translation – it is important. Veryyy important.) Protein is created through 20 different amino acids – nine of which (AKA the essential amino acids) must come from food. The National Academy of Medicine recomends that 10–30% of your diet should consist of protein (Harvard T.C. Chan School of Public Health, n.d.).

Karen Darden, MS, RD explained in a personal interview:

Protein is one of the essential macronutrients that provides our body with both energy and the amino acids needed to create not only muscle and organ tissue but also the enzymes and hormones that help regulate basically every function in our bodies. Protein is found in a wide variety of food sources like eggs, seafood, poultry, dairy, nuts and seeds, beans, lentils, whole grains and other meats. However not all protein sources contain all of the essential amino acids so it is important to make sure you are getting your protein from an assortment of different foods.

It's also important to eat a variety of protein sources – including the ones that your eating disorder might be afraid of!

Karen Darden, MS, RD, says:

There's a lot of information out there on the health benefits and risks of eating certain types of proteins. Red meat and soy have both developed a troublesome reputation. However, these foods have many benefits, red meat is a great source of the easily absorbed form of iron, and soy is a plant protein that contain all the essential amino acids unlike most other plant proteins. In eating disorder recovery, it's important to develop and maintain as much variety in the proteins rich foods you are choosing in order to truly separate out any food fears and rules from true preferences.

Nicole Cruz, RD, explained in a personal interview:

Many people tend to fear red meat. However, red meat offers a rich supply of protein, vitamins and minerals. It also contains saturated fat. Saturated fat is often demonized, but our body requires saturated fat to function. It aids in proper brain function, nerve signaling, and cell structure. Again, it is important to get a variety of fats for overall health.

Jennifer

In my eating disorder I was TERRIFIED of so many foods. Basically, anything that the media labeled as "bad" (which was almost all food) invoked the kind of fear like I was walking alone down a dark sketchy alleyway in the middle of the night. I remember looking in scorn at someone eating a muffin in front of me and thinking, "I wouldn't eat that if you paid me a million dollars!" Well, the joke ended up being on me because not only did I end up eating muffins (and donuts and all the things) but I actually paid a registered dietitian to eat them with me (lol, the irony). One coping technique that I used was googling all of the nutrition benefits of the foods that I was scared of. I would use this information to help challenge my eating disorder voice when it started to get loud. For instance, one of my big fears was anything with fat in it so naturally I was petrified of olive oil (the horror!) I remember reading a mini book on the health benefits of olive oil as one way to try to challenge the unhelpful thoughts in my head. However, simply having that information, by itself, definitely wasn't enough. I also had to work on reaching out for help, using distress tolerance skills, and allllll the exposure therapy (NOT fun but soooo freaking worth it).

Facing Those "Fear Foods"

So now that you are all caught up on the rockstars that are macronutrients, how can you go about beginning to face those fear foods?
    Buckle up friend. We've got you covered.

Fear Food Hiearchy

A great place to start when it comes to challenging fear foods is with what is called a "fear food hierarchy" (Muhlheim, 2020). This is an activity in which you make a list of all of the foods that your eating disorder has caused you to fear, starting with the lowest level of anxiety foods up to the highest (we like to use a 1–10 scale). Then, next to each food, you can write down any eating disorder thoughts.

An example:

Fear Food	Anxiety Level (1–10)	Eating Disorder Thought	Dates Tried

It can be helpful to start with the less anxiety-provoking foods, and to work your way up to the more anxiety-provoking ones. This will help you to build up that confidence. It's also important to repeat the exposures until the anxiety starts to go down. You can log the dates that you do them in the hierarchy too (Muhlheim, 2020).

It might feel incredibly hard and scary at first (things tend to scream when you kill them; bye Felicia (Felicia being your eating disorder)) but the more that you challenge your eating disorder's rules, the easier it will get over time.

Pro Tip: You shouldn't have to face your "fear foods" alone. Getting support can make a *huge* difference.

Examples of who to ask:

• Family members
• Partners
• Friends
• Therapist
• Registered Dietitian
• Mentor

It's also cool to think outside the box and to consider using video platforms if needed, which opens up the possibility of doing meals/snacks with someone who doesn't live nearby.

But What About the Anxiety?

The anxiety struggle can be real when it comes to challenging fear foods. It's important to start to reframe an increase of anxiety and eating disorder thoughts as a sign that you're winning at recovery. (Look at you go, you badass!) When it comes to coping strategies, we have two general kinds: processing and distraction. Processing means working through the issue – i.e. talking about it and exposing yourself to it. Basically, processing means dealing. Distraction is just that – distracting yourself from the issue. The right kind of coping depends on our needs in the moment (i.e. it's probably not best to do a processing strategy at work).

However, we want to make sure that we don't solely do distraction strategies, because it is so, so important to make the time and space to process our emotions (hey, don't roll your eyes at us!).

Processing coping strategies:

- Journaling about how you are feeling.
- Talking to a therapist.
- Talking to a friend.
- Talking to a partner or family member.
- Writing down some of the anxious thoughts and then writing mantras or coping statements under each one.
- Doing artwork around your struggle with anxiety.
- Writing a song or a rap about how you are feeling.
- Writing poetry.

Colleen

So I fought against the idea of changing my thoughts around food for a long time (surprise, surprise). Looking back, I think it was because what I was hearing from my dietitians was fundamentally different from what I was hearing from society. My dietitians were telling me that all foods fit. They were telling me to eat the damn cupcake. Society was telling me that sugar is the devil, and that my orthorexic tendencies were actually really crucial for a long and healthy life. This was confusing (still is sometimes!). For me personally, it was helpful to eventually immerse myself in the anti-diet world. I had to do more than just attend the appointments with dietitians. I had to read the books, listen to the podcasts, and join the Facebook groups. Basically, I had to inundate myself in order to create such a radical shift in my thinking. If you can relate, have some self-compassion! You are swimming up our cultural stream when you are legalizing food. Maybe you, like me, have to go "all in" in terms of the anti-diet world to help you create these shifts in thinking.

Distraction coping strategies:

- Playing with a pet.
- Soothing with your senses: i.e. drinking tea, smelling a candle, wrapping yourself in a blanket, watching a YouTube video of ocean waves.
- Listening to soothing music.
- Window shopping.

- Meditating.
- Going to a coffee shop with a book.
- Naming everything of a color that you can see in the room (i.e. red, blue, etc.).
- Watching your favorite tv-show.
- Watching news bloopers YouTube (trust us, they're great).
- Watching cute animal videos YouTube (we're big animal fans, mmmk?).
- Calling a friend to talk about something not related to your anxiety.

It's important to note that it's totally 100% normal to feel increased anxiety while you are challenging your eating disorder – however, this anxiety is TEMPORARY and will not last for forever.

Some coping strategies I can try:

Processing

1.
2.
3.
4.
5.

Distraction

1.
2.
3.
4.
5.

Journaling Prompts:

1. What are some eating disorder beliefs that you have around carbs, fat, and protein?
2. Write some pro-recovery mantras that you can tell yourself around each of these macronutrients.
3. How would your life be different if you were able to eat ALL foods without guilt or anxiety?
4. What would be some steps that you would have to take in order to get there?
5. What is your definition of food freedom?

References

American Heart Association (n.d.) Dietary fats. www.heart.org/en/healthy-living/healthy-eating/eat-smart/fats/dietary-fats

Bergland, C. (2013, Jan. 22). Cortisol: Why the "stress hormone" is public enemy no. 1. Psychology Today. www.psychologytoday.com/us/blog/the-athletes-way/201301/cortisol-why-the-stress-hormone-is-public-enemy-no-1

Harvard T.C. Chan School of Public Health (n.d.) Protein. www.hsph.harvard.edu/nutritionsource/what-should-you-eat/protein/

Lawrence, S.A. (2016, March 22). Thallium poisoning from kale. Stephen A. Lawrence D.D.S. Inc. www.wellnessdentalcare.com/1526/thallium-poisoning-from-kale/

Mayo Clinic Staff. (2020, April 17). Nutrition and healthy eating. Mayo Clinic. www.mayoclinic.org/healthy-lifestyle/nutrition-and-healthy-eating/in-depth/carbohydrates/art-20045705

Muhlheim, L. (2020, April 25). Facing your fear foods in eating disorder recovery. Verywellmind. www.verywellmind.com/facing-fear-foods-in-eating-disorder-recovery-4114751

Pasquale, M.G.D. (2009). The essentials of essential fatty acids. *Journal of Dietary Supplements*, 6(2): 143–161. doi: 10.1080/19390210902861841

Robinson, J. (2018, Nov. 25). What are symptoms of sun poisoning? WebMD. www.webmd.com/skin-problems-and-treatments/qa/what-are-symptoms-of-sun-poisoning

Rollin, J. (2016a, Oct. 4). 4 reasons why you don't need to fear carbs, according to experts. Huffpost. www.huffpost.com/entry/4-reasons-why-you-dont-need-to-fear-carbs-according_b_57f3cbe9e4b0f482f8f0bdb4

Rollin, J. (2016b, Oct. 20). 3 reasons why you don't need to fear dietary fat, according to experts. Huffpost. www.huffpost.com/entry/3-reasons-why-you-dont-need-to-fear-dietary-fat-according_b_580939b5e4b0b1bd89fdb002

Scott, J.R. (2019, July 17). Calorie definition and why we count them. Verywellfit. www.verywellfit.com/what-is-a-calorie-and-why-should-i-care-3496238

Semeco, A. (2020, May 15). What happens if you drink too much water? Medical News Today. www.medicalnewstoday.com/articles/318619

Warner, J. (2004, July 27). A little fat helps the vegetables go down. WebMD. www.webmd.com/diet/news/20040727/a-little-fat-helps-the-vegetables-go-down#1

5   All about Those Feels
Why Emotions Matter

So here you are. Changing behaviors. Legalizing food. Doin' the recovery thang. Getting your general badassery on. Can we just take a moment to commend your efforts here? Seriously, you are amazing, even if your eating disorder voice is telling your otherwise (which we are willing to bet it is). Right now, the thoughts are likely louder than they have been. You may be thinking, "ok Colleen and Jennifer. This has all been well and good but things are actually worse than before, so what's going on here?"

What's going on is that you are actually *challenging* this voice (maybe for the first time!). Think of your eating disorder as a dictator that has ruled your life for years. What do dictators do when their loyal subjects begin to challenge them? Do they shrink back and say "geez sorry. I never knew you weren't into me. I'll leave now. Bye then"?

Nah. Dictators get LOUDER when people first begin to challenge them. They get angry and desperate and start grabbing for control where they can take it. The same thing happens with an eating disorder voice. It's getting louder because you're disobeying it. This is a *good* thing. So tell that asshole to pipe down for us, ok? In fact, feel free to tell your eating disorder, "thanks but no thanks. I know you are trying to help me in some twisted way, but I got it from here ok?" Don't worry. That voice will quiet eventually.

So now that you're challenging thoughts and changing the behaviors, onto the fun stuff.

Jennifer

Throughout the years, I learned to suppress and numb out from my emotions as a way to cope and over the years I used a variety of different behaviors to achieve this goal. Whether it was drinking, restricting, purging, or compulsive studying – all of these behaviors numbed me out in the short term but only made me even more miserable in the long term. Let's be real here: learning how to let myself feel things and then effectively cope was tough. However, it's made allll the difference. Does it mean that I enjoy feeling unpleasant emotions?

No. But I've learned how to ride "the waves" of my emotions and to recognize that they will all eventually come down on their own if I can sit with them.

Let's Chat Emotions

Disordered eating is largely emotional. You have likely already identified that the way that you act around food is counterintuitive. You have already probably realized that it is not *logical* to be terrified of a banana. And yet – the fear still grips you. The thoughts still feel omnipresent.

That's because logic and thought is only a small part of the equation here. The bigger, more important piece is the *emotional* part that drives the thoughts and behaviors.

Emotions are important. We have them for a reason. In fact, we evolved, as humans, to have emotions all the time. We developed emotions for communication purposes. They are data. They let us know when our needs are not being met. They let other people know how to interact with us. They help us create bonds. In other words, emotions are SUPER important. And yet, our society doesn't seem to think so. Think about it. How much education about our emotions did you receive in school? None? A sentence or two from your health teacher about how your emotions may start to feel "all over the place when puberty hits"? It's wild – our parents and role models were telling us to memorize the preamble to the Declaration of Independence and cramming algebra down our throats, when they should have been telling us about how anger isn't wrong, and that sadness is necessary for joy. Face palm.

Not only does our society not inform us about emotions – it actually tends to demonize them. Correction – society demonizes *certain* emotions. Take sadness for example. We are ok with laughing together, but *crying* in public – horror of horrors! Not in public dear. May we suggest a cozy restroom stall to feel your feels in?

It's just weird when you think about it. Why are certain expressions of affect ok, while others are considered taboo and something to hide? And while we're on the subject of silly lessons that we pick up pertaining to emotions – why are certain emotions gendered? There is no actual data that *shows* that men experience sadness less often than women, or that women do not get angry as often as men. In fact, there is actually some pretty interesting research that suggests that men and women have similar emotional experiences, but women tend to have higher levels of "emotional reactivity" (Deng et al., 2016). We would argue that the difference in emotional reactivity (fancy term for expression) is because our ridiculous society has convinced us that women or femmes are allowed to feel things, but masculine individuals are not. This idea that emotions are gendered in nature is a complete fallacy – created by a society that lives and dies by the binary. Culturally, we shove this message at people from birth – the message that men generally feel less than women, and that when men do feel, it's most likely anger. The other part of this message is that women are more emotional than men. Less logical. More likely to cry at the site of a confusing calculus equation than to – umm – handle it? (What the hell, by the way?)

We're here to set this damn record straight. All humans experience emotions. And there is no recorded evidence that being male, female, non-binary, or gender fluid impacts the intensity of emotions, or which emotions we feel more powerfully. Only internalized lessons from society impact which emotions we express, and which we compartmentalize.

This. This is what gets us into trouble. Our societal misunderstanding of emotions. Our cultural decision to embrace logic and cognition, while ignoring affective wisdom. This messaging has led to more and more of us feeling stuck. Hiding our emotions. Ignoring them. Or, worse yet, pretending that they don't exist.

Because, the thing is, emotions are sort of like beach balls under water. You can hold them down and pretend that they're not there, but eventually your arms will get tired and they are going to pop right up – often more intensity than they were even meant to in the first place! What does "popping up" look like, you ask? Welp, popping up looks like disordered eating. That's why we are harping on this. Because we have found that a lot, and we mean A LOT, of disordered eating stems from efforts to suppress, ignore, or numb out difficult emotional experiences (Wildes et al., 2010). It's important that you consider this in terms of your own journey. What would you be thinking about (and, in turn, feeling) if you were not constantly thinking about restricting your food or losing weight? Take a moment to consider this. Journal your responses in the following space:

If I wasn't constantly thinking about food and my weight, I would likely be thinking about _____

_____, which would leave me feeling_____

_____

If you are like most of our clients (and ok fine, both of us too) you would likely be thinking about some deep, dark stuff if you were not thinking about food and weight. Answers that we have heard to this question:

- If I wasn't constantly thinking about food and my weight, I would likely be thinking about how I am a disappointment as a human.
- If I wasn't constantly thinking about food and my weight, I would likely be thinking about how I have no personality.

- If I wasn't constantly thinking about food and my weight, I would likely be thinking about how much I hate myself.
- If I wasn't constantly thinking about food and my weight, I would likely be thinking about how scary my future is.

Emotions are Important

We were born knowing how to feel emotions – they are important data. What do we mean by this? Well, when we humans were evolving, we developed emotions as communications tools. They help us communicate our needs to others. Think about it. Why do you think we *show* emotions? We cry because crying communicates to others that we are likely in need of support. We furrow our brow and frown when we are angry because it lets others know that we need space, or that a boundary has been violated. Emotions are essential for us, as social creatures. They help us show up for one another. In fact, without emotions, can you imagine how robotic we would all be? Gag (Lynch, 2018).

But emotions are not just helpful socially. Nope. They also help each of us in more *intrinsic* ways. For example, anxiety can motivate us to act. (Recall when you have been anxious about a test, and then studied extra hard for it? Bam. Right there. That is motivation.) Emotions also help us to make decisions – they help us to survive and thrive. Example? Anger helps us to confront. Another example? Fear helps us to avoid. You see, we *need* emotions to live. So why all the denial? Why are we so freakin' into numbing our emotions out?

The answer to that question, friends, is not an easy one. We all fall into the pattern of numbing out emotions for our own reasons. Maybe some of have had absent parents, or parents who told us "it's not cool to be mad" or "pick yourself up and stop crying." It's pretty painful to constantly feel invalidated when you have an emotion, so we work *not to feel*.

Maybe some of us experienced trauma – sexual assaults, severe bullying, family members or friends dying, major upheaval – it's *really* tough to sit with the hard emotions that stem from those experiences. So sometimes – we run.

Colleen

Ok so I used to be an absolute wizard at numbing my emotions. Like if I could have gotten my doctorate in something other than psychology, it would have been numbing. It started in middle school and didn't end until…well to be honest I can *still* fall into the trap of running away from things like loneliness and despair from time to time. And I am not alone in this! My wonderful clients tend to all have this in common as well. That is why one of the main things

I teach (and one of the main things I had to learn during my own recovery) is: feel it. That emotion you are afraid of? You have to stop the running, stop the numbing, and feel it to heal it. Anything else just turns into a half-life.

The truth is, your reason for numbing or ignoring your emotions is totally unique to you. But one thing is for sure – there is no way to live a meaningful life when you are actively, desperately trying to distract yourself from your emotions. A wise friend of ours once said, emotions are like children in a car. You don't really want them in the driver's seat, but you don't want to stuff them in the trunk either.

The most important step to take when it comes to getting back in touch with your emotions is to begin *identifying* your emotions. When you feel sad, angry, lonely – name this for yourself. Work to understand where you feel the emotion in your body, and how you know the emotion is happening.

Then, you'll want to work towards identifying what data this emotion is trying to convey to you. (Try the journaling prompt at the end of this chapter for a starting point.) Once you can name emotions, AND identify their unique purposes, they will not have as much power over you (i.e. they won't be driving the car!).

Journaling Prompt

1. Time for a lil' writing about those damn feels. Next to each emotion, write down the *why* for it – that is, write down how these emotions help you.

   Example:
   Anger helps me to: protect myself, confront danger, and assert my
       boundaries.

   Anger helps me to:

   Sadness helps me to:

   Joy helps me to:

   Guilt helps me to:

   Sorrow helps me to:

   Disgust helps me to:

2) Now comes the tricky part. Next to each emotion, write down the impact of your eating disorder.

Example:
My eating disorder has impacted my ability to feel anger by: enhancing it. I feel angry all of the time. I feel angry instead of sadness or joy.

My eating disorder has impacted my ability to feel anger by:

My eating disorder has impacted my ability to feel sadness by:

My eating disorder has impacted my ability to feel joy by:

My eating disorder has impacted my ability to feel guilt by:

My eating disorder has impacted my ability to feel sorrow by:

My eating disorder has impacted my ability to feel disgust by:

We hope that this exercise allows you to see how your eating disorder has seriously messed with your ability to use your emotional intelligence. Not to worry though – you CAN get back in touch with your emotions, and you CAN learn to listen to them.

References

Deng, Y., Chang, L., Yang, M., Huo, M., & Zhou, R. (2016). Gender differences in emotional response: inconsistency between experience and expressivity. *Plos One*, https://doi.org/10.1371/journal.pone.0158666

Lynch, H. (2018). *The Function of Emotions: Why and When Emotions Help Us*. New York: Springer International Publishing.

Wildes, J., Ringham, R., & Marcus, M. (2010). Emotion avoidance in patients with anorexia nervosa: initial test of a functional model. *International Journal of Eating Disorders*, 43(5): 398–404.

6 Binge Eating

No, It's Not about "Willpower"

Picture this. You just finished dinner, when the food in the pantry starts calling to you: "Yooohoooo. Remember me? I'm here. I'm full. Come visit!" You told yourself that you wouldn't do it again, but all you can think about is washing that damn package of Oreos down with an entire effing carton of milk. Your mind drifts off to getting lost in a jar of peanut butter that you slather over bread. You are itching to eat until you feel completely numb – that familiar feeling of exhausted, detached comfort. You head to the kitchen feeling almost like you're possessed, and the binge begins.

After you binge – yup – here come the feels. You feel guilty, ashamed, and sad. You've told yourself before that it won't happen again but on nights like these, it just feels impossible to stop.

Sound familiar? If so, no shame. ABSOLUTELY no shame allowed here. Because, let's be real here: binge eating is so stigmatized in our culture. However, binge eating disorder (and bulimia) are both serious mental illnesses. And they are NOT about a lack of willpower.

What Classifies as a Binge Anyway?

A binge is eating in a one–two-hour period of time, a much larger quantity of food than is "typical" for someone under the same circumstances. It also has these extra elements of feeling "out of control," eating much faster than usual, feeling overly full, a sense of shame/guilt over the episode, eating alone because of embarrassment, and eating large amounts of food in the absence of physical hunger (American Psychiatric Association, 2013).

Myth Bustin'

There are a TON of myths circling around the topic of binge eating. Seriously. It is one of the most misunderstood disordered eating behaviors of all time. We are ready to debunk these myths and hit ya with some truth bombs.

1.   *People who binge lack willpower.*

We call total BS on this. Binge eating doesn't have to do with "willpower" or discipline, rather it's a symptom of a mental illness. It is no more "a choice" than any other mental illness.

2.   *You can tell who is struggling with binge eating by looking at them.*

Hard no. People who struggle with binge eating come in all shapes, sizes, ethnicities, genders, abilities, races, ages, and socioeconomic statuses. Eating disorders do not discriminate and you can't tell who is struggling simply by looking at them.

3.   *In order to recover from binge eating disorder or bulimia you simply need to be "more disciplined" with food.*

Eating disorders are not about "discipline," they are mental illnesses and this is actually a surefire way to make things even worse. Trying to control your food *more* is NEVER the answer to recovering from any eating disorder.

Out of the Shadows

SO MANY of these myths can serve to exacerbate the shame and secrecy, which helps to keep binge eating alive. But do you want to hear an honest truth that we wish someone had told us when we were struggling? Binge eating is actually a *resilient* way to try to cope with past trauma, intense emotions, feelings of low self-worth, and a variety of other things. Yup. We said resilient. You have been doing the best that you could – coping with this one skill that you happened upon (i.e. bingeing). And it's not your fault that you are struggling.

An analogy that we like to give is imagine that binge eating is a warm winter coat. It helped you to survive when you lived somewhere in freezing temperatures. However, you have since moved to California and are still wearing the coat. You feel trapped and uncomfortable. The thing that once saved you is no longer helping – and is actually getting in the way.

Binge Eating Triggers

1. Restriction (Physical and Emotional)

Truth bomb: one big trigger for bingeing is restriction. There are two types of restriction.

Physical Restriction

Not eating enough to meet your energy needs. Yes, this includes following a diet plan or telling yourself you can only eat under a certain number of calories. It might also include cutting certain foods out of your diet.

Emotional Restriction

Eating something but feeling shame/guilt/anxiety while eating it. Telling yourself that this will be "the last time" you eat this – and that you'll "be good" again tomorrow. That's right – you don't have to actually physically restrict food for it to be restriction. Shaming yourself actually has a pretty similar psychological effect.

The reality is that back in the Stone Age when food was relatively scarce – our bodies evolved to respond to famine by eating as much as possible at the next food encounter. This helped to ensure our survival as a species. Bingeing was a healthy response to periods of famine (Muhlheim, 2019). In other words? Your body is wired to respond to restriction by bingeing – you aren't lacking "willpower."

2. Habituation

Have you ever had the experience where you were driving somewhere that you've been a million times before and when you got to the location you said "holy shit. I have no memory of getting here." Freaky, right? This is basic-ally what happens when we do something on "autopilot" because it's become so habitual and engrained. So, apply this idea to bingeing. Your brain can become wired into automatic loops where you start to associate one thing with another, i.e. get home, eat dinner, binge. Binge eating can become habitual for people, and part of recovery is learning how to break this habit loop.

3. Emotional Triggers (AKA All the Feels)

Many people binge as a way to try to cope with intense emotions. Our clients will describe that bingeing provides them with a feeling of comfort, anxiety relief, and distraction. AKA: Bingeing "works" in the short term. We need to show up for this fact and not sugarcoat things. But – and this is an important "but" – in the long-term bingeing often leads to increased shame, depression, anxiety, and isolation.

4. The "F*ck It" Mentality

"I was good all day. Then dinner came around and I just felt like I blew it. So I said f*ck it – and binged." If we had a penny for every time a client shared this with us, we could probably retire. (Ok that's a dramaticization. We'd have a lot of pennies though.) Clients will describe this sense of trying to be "good" (their words, not ours!) all day when it comes to food and then eating something that they feel badly about eating – which then triggers them to say, "f*ck it" and binge. It's the idea of "I've already messed up with my eating, so I might as well binge." This is classic black and white thinking – and another example of emotional restriction that triggers bingeing.

5. The "Don't Binge" Trap

This one might seem strange – but telling yourself "I'm not going to binge. I'm not going to binge" can make it seem *even more appealing.* The "don't binge trap" is when you are sitting on your hands trying so hard not to binge, but it's all that you are thinking about doing. Instead, of trying other coping strategies your mind is one-track focused on "not bingeing." This can trigger a sort of "rebellious teen" eating disorder response.

Your Bingeing Triggers

Do any of these bingeing triggers resonate with ya?
   List the ones that do in the following list:

1.

2.

3.

4.

5.

Recovery From Binge Eating

Action Plan

1. Ditch That Damn Scale

Unless you are being blind weighed by a treatment team, there is simply NO good reason for you to step on the scale. When you recover from binge eating, your body might get smaller, bigger, or stay the same. However, a focus on intentional weight loss is incredibly harmful and can fuel the disorder.
   Pro tip: did you know that you can decline to be weighed at the doctor's office? It is well within your right to ask not to be weighed. Letting go of the scale's power over you is one important step in any recovery journey.
   You don't need a piece of metal to tell you whether you are good enough – you already are!

2. Eliminate Restriction

If you can, try to find a Health At Every Size® eating disorder diet-itian who can assess your intake to make sure that you are eating enough throughout the day. Make a list of foods that you usually avoid or feel guilt and shame around – then challenge yourself to "give yourself permission" to have them in your diet.

You may choose to start by having these foods while out if you are sort of nervous about bringing them into the house (which is an important step to work towards! For real – trying not to have these foods in the house will only make the bingeing worse over time. Trust us). So, for instance, you might start by grabbing ice cream out with a friend.

Write down some mantras that you can tell yourself if guilt or shame comes up around eating a certain food – for example: "all foods can fit into a healthy diet."

Mantras for Food Guilt

3. Rewire Those Neutral Pathways

Alright friends. Let's imagine that there are two paths in a forest. Right now, the binge path is cleared away of brush, carefully tread, and easy to walk down. Sometimes you might walk down it without even realizing! The other path (AKA using alternate coping strategies) is covered with brush and not very easy to walk down. However, with time and practice eventually this path CAN become the new automatic one.

Each time you are able to practice using other coping strategies instead of bingeing, you strengthen the new pathway in your brain. Now people – listen up. We are not saying that this is easy, BUT, it is 100% doable, especially with time, practice, and new skills. Need some ideas about which skills to try? Check it:

SELF COACHING

Practice coaching yourself, i.e. talking back to the eating disorder. Eating disorder therapist and author Carolyn Costin talks about speaking back to the "eating disorder self" from your "healthy self" (Costin et al., 2011). She also suggests dialoguing (i.e. writing out your thoughts) between the two as a way of strengthening your "healthy self" (Costin et al., 2011).

We've seen clients learn how to talk back to their eating disorder thoughts in the moment, and it can be so powerful.

REACHING OUT TO PEOPLE INSTEAD OF YOUR EATING DISORDER

We know that when you're deeply struggling with an eating disorder often the urge is to isolate yourself. However, reaching out to people when you feel pulled to use eating disorder behaviors can be a SUPER useful tool. This was something that we both found to be extremely helpful in our recovery processes.

List who you could reach out to in those moments. Pro tip: this can include a treatment team member.

1.

2.

3.

THE PAUSE SKILL.

Hey – Jennifer here! I created this acronym for coping with urges to binge known as the PAUSE Skill (Rollin, 2018).

P. Pause   At the first sign of an urge to binge coming on, take a moment to pause. Take a deep breath. Tell yourself that you are going to try the PAUSE skill – and that you can still binge after, but that even if you try this skill before bingeing it's still a "win."

A. Allow Space   Remove yourself from the environment (i.e. kitchen) that might be triggering or exacerbating the binge urges. Find somewhere where you can sit down. Remind yourself that you are just practicing creating some space between urge and action.

Check in with yourself and identify whether you are feeling physically hungry. If so, choose to sit down and to eat something mindfully (AKA ask yourself what taste, temperature, and texture of food you are craving and try to find a good match) (Matz & Frankel, 2014). If you are not physically hungry, continue with the rest of the skill.

U. Use Other Coping Skills and Statements   Different strategies will work for different people so this is your chance to explore what works for you. This is likely not the time to process your emotions (because this can intensify binge urges in the moment). However, using some alternate coping strategies can be helpful. I recommend choosing five–ten coping strategies that you can use (for at least ten minutes each) prior to bingeing.

Coping Statement Ideas:

- If I still want to binge eat after I can, but for now I'm going to practice sitting with this urge for ten minutes.
- Each time I practice using the PAUSE skill, it will get easier in the future.
- Binge eating will make me feel better for three minutes, and then I always feel worse after.
- I am more powerful than my eating disorder.
- No amount of food is going to solve this emotional problem.
- I deserve to be kind and compassionate with myself (Rollin, 2018).

Add a few of your own coping statements here:

•

•

S. Separate Your Eating Disorder Thoughts and Urges   Practice separating out your eating disorder thoughts from those of your authentic self. Your eating disorder will say ANYTHING it needs to in order to get you to binge. Think about how you might respond to a loved one who was sharing those same thoughts. Just because you have an urge does NOT mean that you need to act on it. Urges will naturally rise and peak on their own – so long as we are able to practice sitting with them. The more that you are able to not give in to the urge, the easier that it will get over time.

You could start by setting a timer for five minutes and practicing sitting with the urge to binge – and then gradually extending it out over time. Remind yourself that bingeing may feel like it "works" in the short term. However, in the long term it only leads to increased misery and unhappiness.

E. Enlist Help From a Supportive Person   We can hear the pushback already – but we PROMISE you aren't burdening the people who truly care about you. So, think about who you can reach out to if the binge urges are feeling really intense. You don't even have to talk about the urges if you don't want to. You could instead engage in a conversation as a means of distraction while you ride out the urge.

Even if you reach out and the person does not respond – you've still brought your authentic self to the forefront by reaching out and put some space between urge and action. Pretty badass if you ask us.

Coping with Emotions

SO many people binge as a way to try to numb out from unpleasant emotions. So, it is important to figure out some other ways of processing and coping with emotions.

Listen up. Studies have shown that most emotions last for 90 seconds if we are able to sit with them (and don't try to interfere!) (Heisler, 2013). Ninety. Seconds. When we frame it like this, emotions don't sound so scary, do they?

Therapy with an eating disorder clinician can be one way to learn how to process and express emotions in a healthy way. Journaling or doing art around your emotions can also be great outlets.

You can also start to reframe how you view emotions in the first place. Like we've mentioned, emotions are simply messengers in the body that have come to tell us something. Rather than trying to numb out or run from them – invite them in, get to know them, and then gradually watch them lose their grip over you. This doesn't mean that you will no longer feel intense emotions – rather that you won't be afraid or avoidant of them.

Self-Compassion

Self-compassion throughout the recovery process is key. Remind yourself that you are likely bingeing as a result of restriction (physical and/or emotional), emotional factors, and/or past trauma. You are doing the best you can to cope with the circumstances in your life – AND you can learn more values – aligning ways to cope.

Struggling with binge eating disorder or bulimia is NOT your fault. Not even a little bit, friends. You aren't broken or "lacking willpower"; you are doing your best to try to survive. Shaming yourself for bingeing only keeps the cycle going.

So instead, think about how you'd treat and speak to someone that you love.

The next time that you want to beat yourself up for bingeing, try putting your hand over your heart and saying kind and nurturing words to yourself. Yeah – it sounds corny. AND we want you to try it anyway. What the hell do you have to lose? *Snaps fingers and sings* Gettin' corny with it (to the tune of "Getting jiggy with it").

Another exercise is to find a picture of yourself as a little kid and think about what you'd want to say to him/her/them. Then, practice saying those same kind and supportive words to yourself.

Journaling Prompts

1. What are your main bingeing triggers?
2. What are some steps that you can take to start putting the action plan discussed into place?
3. What is the function of bingeing for you? (i.e. to take a break, comfort, calm?)
4. Next to each function write some more values – aligning ways that you could get those same needs met.
5. Write down five ways that you can practice being kinder to yourself this week.

References

American Psychiatric Association. (2013). *Diagnostic and Statistical Manual of Mental Disorders*, Fifth Edition. Arlington, VA: Author.

Costin, C., Grabb, G.S., & Rothschild, B. (2011). *8 Keys to Recovery from an Eating Disorder: Effective Strategies from Therapeutic Practice and Personal Experience (8 Keys to Mental Health)*. W.W. Norton & Company.

Heisler, M. (2016, April. 6). Why Stay Angry? Huffpost. www.huffpost.com/entry/why-stay-angry_b_9602104

Matz, J. & Frankel, E. (2014). *Beyond a Shadow of a Diet: The Comprehensive Guide to Treating Binge Eating Disorder, Compulsive Eating, and Emotional Overeating*. Routledge.

Muhlheim, L. (2019, Nov. 4). Understanding the binge cycle: the role of dieting. National Rehabs Directory. www.rehabs.com/pro-talk/understanding-the-binge-eating-cycle-the-role-of-dieting/

Rollin, J. (2018, Jan. 18). What to do when you want to binge eat. HuffPost. www.huffpost.com/entry/what-to-do-when-you-want-to-binge-eat_b_5a54a566e4b0ee59d41c0dba

7 Health at Every Size
The MVP of Eating Disorder Recovery

Y'all – there's this concept called Health at Every Size that we have found to be a real game-changer when it comes to recovery. When we stumbled upon the Health At Every Size® (HAES®) movement, it transformed our lives personally and professionally. We call HAES the MVP (the most valuable player) of eating disorder recovery because we feel that it's one of the key elements of eating disorder treatment.

A Note on Language

The language that we use matters. We reject the terms "o*erweight" (over what weight?) and "o*ese" as we feel that these words are stigmatizing towards those in larger bodies.

Instead, we will be using language such as "person in a larger body" and "fat."

Some individuals in larger bodies have chosen to reclaim the word "fat" (similarly to those in the LGBTQIA2S+ movement reclaiming the word "queer") as a neutral descriptor, much like the words "tall" and "short." We support this, and want this book to serve as a step towards destigmatizing and neutralizing "fat."

*Please note: unfortunately some of the research studies that we discuss will reference the "o" words. Le sigh. Thanks fat-phobic academia.

BMI: The Bullshit Measuring Index

Let's chat a little bit about BMI, shall we? The body mass index (BMI) was created in the 19th century by Lambert Adolphe Jacques Quetelet, who was a mathematician (not a doctor!) (Devlin, 2009). He originally created this formula to classify people as part of a research study – it was NEVER meant to be a measure of health (Devlin, 2009).

Also, fun fact in the 1990s: a bunch of Americans went to bed and woke up suddenly "o*erweight." Their body size hadn't changed – however, *against* recommendations from the World Health Organization, an "o*esity task force" (which was funded by the makers of a weight-loss drug: no shocker there) decided to lower the BMI threshold. Face palm (Kennelly, 2010).

So, what the heck is the problem with BMI?

BMI tells us NOTHING about someone's health, happiness, or their relationship to food and their body. It doesn't account for body composition, behaviors, or mental health – and is a poor predictor of someone's overall health and well-being. It categorizes some people as "o*ese" (code for "medically unhealthy") without any further information about their actual health status. It creates a so-called "disease state" out of a body size.

The same way people can be thin and unhealthy, individuals can be fat and healthy.

Body diversity is real and even if we all ate and exercised the same, we'd have different body sizes ('sup genetics?). The same way that dogs come in different shapes and sizes (and we still find them cute!) humans do too. Ultimately, you simply can't evaluate a person's health status based on their BMI.

Colleen

The MVP of recovery. The.freaking.mic drop. Health at Every Size! You want to hear something sad? I didn't hear a single thing about Health at Every Size during grad school. I found out what it was by digging around eating disorder professional Facebook groups after graduating. As soon as I heard what it was, something just clicked for me. I understood why recovery had been such a daunting, horrific uphill battle – because I had been recovering from an illness in which I idealized thinness into a society that did just that as well! I was fearful of becoming fat, as was the WHOLE WORLD THAT I LIVED IN. Why didn't any of my therapists or dietitians address this with me? It would have been so helpful to have had someone sit me down and say: "Look. I get it. We are asking you to basically defy societal ideas and give a big f-you to the entire field of medicine (which is constantly pushing the "o*esity epidemic" fear mongering on us). But the truth is, fatness isn't something to fear. And healthy bodies come in a huge range of sizes and weights. Let's work to help you build resiliency so that you can ward off society's fat-phobic messages instead of just throwing coping skills at you." But I didn't have anyone say that to me. So here I am. Saying it to you now. Hoping that hearing this will help you to feel that things "click" in your recovery as well.

Set Point Theory

Your set point is a range, generally of 10–20 pounds, that your body will fight to maintain (Thompson, 1997). When your weight dips below your set point range, your body will adjust metabolism and appetite to try to get you back to your set point (Thompson, 1997).

Truth bomb: Your set point range is largely based on genetics (Thompson, 1997). The same way that some people are shorter or taller, some people are naturally larger or smaller. Set point can also shift throughout our lifetime. And here's the thing: Your body doesn't read magazines or scroll through Instagram. It doesn't know the weight that society is saying you *should* be. It simply fights to keep you alive and works to maintain a body weight that is healthiest for *you*.

Ultimately, the same way that you don't need to try to regulate your breathing or when you use the bathroom – your body will naturally regulate your weight for you.

Your Ideal Weight

So what is your ideal weight? (Hint: it likely isn't what you think.)

Your ideal weight is the one where you can go out for brunch and laugh with friends over pancakes. It's where you can travel, explore new cultures, and be truly present in the moment. It's when you can fully engage in relationships because you're no longer consumed with thoughts about food. It's whatever weight your body ends up at when you are free from disordered behaviors around food and exercise and you can *fully engage* in your life.

SO when you spend most of your time trying to suppress your body below your natural weight range, this will keep you stuck in recovery – and ultimately in your life.

About That Research

The dominant societal narrative is that fat=unhealthy and thin=healthy. But this assumption is problematic and flawed. We can't wait to share some of the research around weight science with you.

Myth: Being in a Larger Body Means That You Will Die Sooner

One big assumption is that being in a larger body=increased mortality (and that thinner people live longer) and this is simply *not supported* by the data. For instance,

> most epidemiological studies find that people who are overweight or moderately obese live at least as long as normal weight people, and often longer. Analysis of the National Health and Nutrition Examination

Surveys I, II, and III, which followed the largest nationally representative cohort of United States adults, determined that greatest longevity was in the overweight category.

(Bacon & Aphramor, 2011)

Further, there is something known as "the o*esity paradox" where individuals in larger bodies have been shown to have *better* health outcomes (including lower mortality rates) than their thinner counterparts when it comes to a variety of diseases including coronary heart disease, chronic heart failure, stroke, and type 2 diabetes (Hainer & Aldhoon-Hainerová, 2013).

Myth: Losing Weight Means That You Will Be Healthier

In Health At Every Size, Dr. Lindo Bacon states "No one has ever proved that losing weight prolongs life" (Bacon, 2010, p. 140). Furthermore, the National Institutes of Health held a conference regarding dieting and said that "most studies, and the strongest science, shows weight loss…is actually strongly associated with increased risks of death-by as much as several hundred percent" (Bacon, 2010).

Now, this is not to say that correlation equals causation. For instance, there could be other factors such as weight cycling, and the methods that people used to try to lose weight, which contributed to these outcomes (Bacon, 2010).

Is your mind starting to churn yet? We know ours did as we started to learn more about weight science. Interesting, right? The reality is that so many of the ideas that we see as "accepted facts" are really just false or over-exagerated narratives that have been pushed by the diet industry.

Weight Stigma

What is weight stigma? Essentially, it's sterotypes, biases, and judgments made against a person because of their weight, which is SO not ok. The reality is that individuals in larger bodies often face systemic forms of oppression (we're looking at you, tiny airplane seats) alongside judgment from society at large. For instance, if you think about popular media, characters in larger bodies are often depicted as comic relief, unattractive, and/or unintelligent.

Examples of Weight Stigma

- Believing that those in larger bodies are "lazy" and "unintelligent."
- Medical providers dismissing someone's health concerns and saying that "weight loss" is the solution for everything.
- Seating that does not accomodate a diverse range of body sizes.
- Assuming that someone in a larger body is unhealthy.

An Exercise:

It's SO important to start to unpack any biases that you might have around those in larger bodies (or possibly internalized fatphobia if you are in a larger body yourself).

It's also crucial to be compassionate with yourself – as these biases are ingrained into the fabric of our society, and we all grew up in diet culture. You are not "bad" or "wrong" for having biases and it takes courage to be willing to start to explore them.

Take a moment and write down any words/thoughts/feelings that come to mind around these two words:

Thin

Fat

It's important to note that the same way that you learned these messages through diet culture, role modeling, or other messaging, you can also unlearn them.

We both had thin privilege and also struggled with fatphobia when we were sick with our eating disorders (and we continue to have thin privilege now that we are recovered as well). Starting to unpack that was crucial towards our recovery. We also want to note that because of thin privilege we did not face the added layer of weight stigma from society when we were trying to recover (which is so messed up, and a reason why we must all continue to fight against fatphobia. People in all body sizes deserve the right to recovery and feel safe in their bodies).

A Note on Thin Privilege

So, you've heard us mention it a few times now and you might be asking, well, what the heck is thin privilege?

Thin privilege does NOT mean that you don't suffer or struggle, rather it means that you do not struggle with *weight stigma from society*. Examples of weight stigma from society could be not fitting into airplane seats, having to shop in speciality stores to find clothing that fits, and being told by doctors that you need to lose weight (when you come in for a damn sore throat).

We hope that this chapter helps to debunk some of the myths and sterotypes that you might be aware of (or have internalized) regarding those in larger bodies.

Weight Stigma in Eating Disorder Treatment

We want to yell it from the rooftops – you can struggle with a serious eating disorder at ANY weight!

Unfortunatly, eating disorder professionals are not immune to weight stigma and it shows up sometimes in eating disorder treatment.

So, we want to start by debunking a few myths.

1. *You can tell what kind of eating disorder someone struggles with by their body size.*

False! You can have any kind of eating disorder at *any* weight (i.e. binge eating disorder in a smaller body and anorexia in a larger body).

Technically the Diagnostic and Statistical Manual labels those who have anorexia but are not deemed as "underweight" per BMI (BS measuring index) as having "aytpical anorexia" but we think there's nothing aytpical about it (read: more BS and weight stigma here!).

2. *My eating disorder is less serious because I'm in a larger body.*

No. No. No. First off, all eating disorders are serious.

Secondly, your body size does not really tell us about the severity of your eating disorder. You can have a severe eating disorder at *any* weight.

Examples of Weight Stigma in Eating Disorder Treatment

- Body tracing exercises (just, why!?).
- A provider reassuring a client that they won't "let the client get fat."
- Assuming that clients in larger bodies should recieve treatment at a specific binge eating disorder unit.
- When a provider assumes that someone's eating disorder is "less serious" on the basis of their body size.

Weight stigma in eating disorder treatment has got to go. It's absolutely not ok. We want to make sure that you understand – it is *incredibly* important that you are not working with fat-phobic providers, as they can ultimately collude with your eating diorder voice unknowingly.

If you are seeking out a treatment team, it is important to ask them if they work from a Health At Every Size® perspective, and what their understanding of this paradigm is.

Health At Every Size

Ok! Now – are you ready to change the game when it comes to your recovery? Yes? Enter: Health at Every Size (**Rocky* theme song plays in background*). Health At Every Size is a movement that aims to help people of ALL sizes to learn how to compassionately take care of themselves (Bacon, 2010).

The Health At Every Size® Principles:

1. Weight Inclusivity

HAES supports people of ALL bodies, weights, shapes, and sizes. It is a weight-inclusive movement that supports advocating against weight stigma and bias (Association for Size Diversity and Health, n.d).

2. Health Enhancement

Rather than focusing on weight loss, HAES focuses on health enhancing behaviors (in addition to policies that improve access to care). It also seeks to expand the defintion of health to include emotional, physical, spiritual, economic, and other needs (Association for Size Diversity and Health, n.d.).

3. Respectful Care

HAES advocates work to combat weight stigma. HAES also looks at intersectionality in terms of sexual orientation, gender, socioeconomic status, race, ability, age, socioeocnomic status, and other factors that could interplay with someone's experience of weight stigma (Association for Size Diversity and Health, n.d.).

Intersectionality: is the way in which different forms of discrimination overlap – especially as it applys to those in marginalized groups, i.e. being both a female and a woman of color (Merriam-Webster, n.d.).

4. Eating for Well-Being

HAES promotes flexible, joyful, attuned eating – rather than dieting or efforts at weight suppression (Association for Size Diversity and Health, n.d.).

5. Life Enhancing Movement

HAES supports individuals of all sizes, abilities, and preferences in engaging in a joyful movement. It also recognizes the need for rest and self-care, as well as removing any weight loss focus from the movement (Association for Size Diversity and Health, n.d.).

HAES is a movement that aims in giving up the war on your body and instead making peace with your body, food, and movement (Bacon, 2010). Dr. Bacon sums it up best by saying,

> The only way to solve the weight problem is to stop making weight a problem – to stop judging ourselves and others by our size. Weight is not an effective measure of attractivness, moral character or health. The real enemy is weight stigma.
>
> (Bacon, 2010)

Jennifer

I'm not being dramatic when I say that discovering the Health At Every Size® movement changed my life. I was scrolling through Facebook one day when I stumbled upon it. At first, I was a bit confused because it was all new to me. However, the more that I read up on the movement, the more that it started to make sense. Health at Every Size is probably what had the biggest impact on my recovery and also my career as an eating disorder therapist! I am so grateful that I stumbled upon it years ago. It still boggles my mind when other eating disorder professionals say that they don't believe in Health at Every Size – given that it's about helping people of all sizes to take compassionate care of themselves – umm how can you be against that?!

HAES Is Not "Healthy at Every Size"

It's important to not let your eating disorder twist Health At Every Size to mean Healthy at Every Size.

HAES does not suggest that someone is necessarily healthy at their current size (so if you're under your natural weight, for instance, that is not healthy). Rather, it's a weight inclusive approach to well-being. Basically, HAES is referring to everyone's right to pursue health without weight stigma getting in the way. It's also important to note that health is in NO WAY a barometer of someone's worth and that many people struggle with chronic illnesses and will never be "healthy." In other words: Your worth as a human being is not tied to your health status, mmmk?

Expanding Your Definition of Health

Health is not just about food and movement. There are a ton of other factors to health that are often ignored. Health can include physical, emotional, relational, spiritual, sleep, stress, and a variety of other factors.

If you are avoiding certain foods (leading to anxiety/guilt/shame) and casting judgment around food, this is NOT healthy. In fact, this type of mentality will increase the stress hormone (hello cortisol!) (Mayo Clinic Staff, 2019) and is also just exhausting as hell. Additionally, if you are fixated on food, exercise, and weight, it's likely that you are neglecting important aspects of health, i.e. mental health, relational, and emotional – not good people!

Getting Started – Your HAES Journey

We've been brainwashed since childhood to have beliefs about thinness and fatness, which are total cultural constructions. What's a cultural construction? Glad you asked! A cultural construction is a concept that was entirely made up by society. A good example of this would be gender norms (i.e. the idea that little girl's rooms are pink and little boy's rooms are blue). We weren't born believing this – we were taught these ideas through our culture.

In our culture, thinness is currently seen as a sign of beauty. However, there have been time periods in our country's history where fatness was seen as beautiful. For instance, in the 15th and 16th centuries, being large was seen as a sign of beauty and wealth (Hollander, 1977).

In other countries and cultures, the standards of beauty may be different. For instance, in an African tribe called Mauritania, young girls are force fed extreme amounts of food because fatness is seen as a sign of beauty (Haworth, 2011).

BUT – the same way that we've learned to value and aspire to thinness, this can also be unlearned. The first step is to remove any messaging (or set boundaries around it!) in your life that reinforces the thin ideal standard of beauty. Of course, we can't totally get rid of it, but we can look at the books, movies, articles, social media accounts, podcasts, and people that we surround ourselves with.

The next step is to begin to add in Health at Every Size® content through reading books, listening to podcasts, checking out the research articles, and finding a community of others (even if it's online!) who are supporters of the HAES® movement.

Doing this made a huge difference for us in terms of our recoveries, and we have seen it make a difference with many of our clients as well!

Journaling Prompts:

1. How could a HAES® perspective help you in terms of your recovery?

2. What are some of your barriers (if any) towards embracing a HAES® perspective?
3. When you were growing up, what messages were you given around body sizes?
4. How do these messages impact you today?
5. In order to start to embody HAES® messaging, what are a few steps that you could take this week? (You can think of some of the specific principles and how you might take small steps towards implementing them.)

References

Association for Size Diversity and Health (n.d.) The health at every size® approach. www.sizediversityandhealth.org/content.asp?id=19

Bacon, L. (2010). *Health At Every Size: The Surprising Truth About Your Weight.* BenBella Books.

Bacon, L., & Aphramor, L. (2011). Weight science: evaluating the evidence for a paradigm shift. *Nutrition Journal, 10, 9.* https://doi.org/10.1186/1475-2891-10-9

Devlin, K. (Host). (2009, July 4). Top 10 reasons why the BMI is bogus [Audio Podcast]. Retrieved from www.npr.org/

Hainer, V. & Aldhoon-Hainerová, I. (2013). Obesity paradox does exist. *Diabetes Care, 36,* 2, S276–S281. https://doi.org/10.2337/dcS13-2023

Haworth, A. (2011, July 21). Forced to be fat. Marie Claire. www.marieclaire.com.au/force-feeding-in-africa

Hollander, A. (1977, Oct. 23). When fat was in fashion. The New York Times. www.nytimes.com/1977/10/23/archives/when-fat-was-in-fashion-abundant-flesh-was-a-thing-of-beauty-to.html

Kennelly, S. (2010, November 25). Weight wars: Nutrition expert says you can be fat but fit. CN & R. https://www.newsreview.com/chico/content/weight-wars/1880478/

Mayo Clinic Staff. (2019, March 19). Chronic stress puts your health at risk. Mayo Clinic. www.mayoclinic.org/healthy-lifestyle/stress-management/in-depth/stress/art-20046037

Merriam-Webster. (n.d.). Intersectionality. In Merriam-Webster.com dictionary. www.merriam-webster.com/dictionary/intersectionality

Thompson, C. (1997). Set point theory. Mirror Mirror. https://mirror-mirror.org/recovery/set-point-theory

8   Fat Positivity

A Game Changer

So, in eating disorder recovery, body acceptance is often seen as a hall marker of recovery. And body acceptance is so key! (You'll hear more about this in the body image chapter.) But body acceptance is one step short of where we are hoping you can eventually land. We want to introduce you to a concept called fat positivity.

The modern-day fat positivity movement can be traced back to the fat-acceptance movement that began in the 1960s as a way to advocate against the discrimination and stigma that larger bodied people faced in America. This movement pushed for acceptance of body diversity, with a main message being that individuals in larger bodies who self-identify as "fat" (reclaiming it as a neutral descriptor like "tall" and "short") are JUST as worthy and deserving as individuals in smaller bodies (Fletcher, 2009).

One of the early groups, The National Association to Advance Fat Acceptance, was started by Bill Fabrey who had grown tired of the discrimination that his larger-bodied wife faced.

It is undeniable. Individuals in larger bodies are often discriminated against in our culture. There are many horrifying cultural stereotypes and false beliefs about fat people, including that they are "lazy," "that they overeat," and that they are "not motivated" (Puhl & Heuer, 2010). (What. The. Hell.)

These false and harmful stereotypes fail to take into account the idea of body diversity. The same way that dogs come in all different shapes and sizes (and we think they're all cute!), humans do too. There simply isn't "one body type that we are all meant to have," despite the harmful narratives from diet culture.

Additionally, we simply shouldn't be shaming anyone based upon their body size or appearance. All we can tell by looking at a someone in a larger body is that they are in a larger body. That's it. And weight stigma (i.e. discrimination and stereotyping that occurs against people in larger bodies) can have adverse health outcomes and is rarely addressed in conversations about health and well-being.

We want to go one step further from fat acceptance and talk about its daughter – fat positivity. Fat positivity is a concept that goes beyond the idea of acceptance and talks about embracing and celebrating ALL bodies – including people in larger bodies who self-identify as fat. Fat positivity is an important goal to embrace during your recovery. While it may not feel innate at first, over time, it will actually likely become a natural progression – body hatred, to body neutrality, to body acceptance, to fat acceptance, and finally, to fat positivity.

The following are essays from folks from various walks of life who identify as living in larger bodies. They have graciously agreed to share their journeys towards fat positivity with us.

Kate Dansie, LCSW-C

Therapist

I was in sixth grade when I realized my body was a little different than the other girls my age. A friend of mine sighed: "we're just sick of the boys calling us flatty." The boys never called me flatty. I looked with envy at her tiny waist. At home, I watched my Mom look in the mirror in despair, sighing "I've just got to lose weight." I remember seeing Slim Fast in the grocery cart. She'd drink a can for lunch with some yogurt and sliced bananas. Sometimes, she'd point to other women: "am I as big as that lady?" "No, Mom" I'd say. The funny thing was: I never really noticed my Mom's body. I did, however, notice her sadness and anxiety about her weight. There were other challenges at home, too. My sister struggled with her mood. My Dad, fiercely hard-working, kind, and loving, could also be intensely angry. Much like my Dad, I had emotional intensity, but with everyone else's struggles there was no room for my feelings. I didn't know what to do with them. I simultaneously wanted help and invisibility. I wanted to be smaller.

By eighth grade I'd fully developed, and like most of the women in my family I, too, was curvy and round. I ached for the power and confidence I imagined thin would bring. I'd look in the mirror at my 13-year-old complexion. Glasses, braces, and fat looked back. I looked to my friends for reassurance. Really, I was body checking. "I'm fat," I'd say. "You are *not* fat!" my friends would reassure in reply: over, and over, and over.

An anaphylactic allergic reaction the summer before my junior year of high school left me terrified to eat. My list of safe foods and safe places to eat got smaller and smaller. My weight dropped dramatically. That fall, a teacher didn't recognize me when I said hello in the hallway. Later, when taking attendance, she made a startling comment: "Why Kate Dansie! You lost weight this summer." Humiliated, another part of me proud, I gave a small nod. "Well, did you?" she pressed. I nodded again and she stopped asking. Later I would recognize that this was a perfect example of the way eating disorders are reinforced.

In college, at the urging of my friends, I finally entered therapy. "Your body image is distorted," my therapist said. "Focus on how you feel," she said. I didn't believe her when she said my body image was distorted, but I let myself do what she suggested. I finally had permission to eat based on something other than how thin I was feeling that day.

I found myself in a sort of half-recovery, and I began to think. Most of my psychology classes were all the way across campus. I pushed myself, and I made it to class, but there were so many days I felt weak. Then, on a hot September day at a barn where I took riding lessons, I passed out. Could I really live like this? Was this sustainable? My friends were steadfast in their support of me, but their frustration and worry wore on them.

I never really wanted full recovery: restricting felt safe, like a little bit of anesthesia in a world that felt frightening. For someone with my anxiety and emotional makeup, it felt really frightening. And yet, as safe as restricting felt, it cost a lot too. I knew there had to be more. I began to imagine my life working as a therapist, and maybe, down the road, as a wife and Mother too. Could I be to someone else what my therapist was to me? Could I give someone that space, a place where all their feelings were allowed? I could see it. I wanted it so much more than I wanted to feel that false confidence, that fake sense of safety. Suddenly, recovery was worth it.

As I found my stride, my body did get bigger. It was hard at first. My therapist, who indeed was skilled and well-meaning, said "are you still exercising?" My Mom, too, meant well, and her response was much worse: "Well, you look like you've gained some weight. Let's work on it together." My friends had their chorus "you're not fat." They saved my life. And yet, I often can't help but wonder how the trajectory of my life would have changed if someone had responded differently to my words "I'm fat." I wish someone had said: "Okay. Maybe as you recover the size of your body will go up. Maybe that's where your body is most comfortable. What does that mean? Who cares? What are your dreams? What footprint do you want to leave on the world?"

Where does fat positivity fit into eating disorder recovery? No one can recover without it. I believed at one time that a smaller body was the only way to get what I wanted. What I didn't realize was that as the size of my body expanded, the size of my life would too. I graduated college with degrees in Psychology and English. I finished my Master's Degree in Social Work. I became a therapist. I met the man who is now my husband, and we have a beautiful daughter. And my friends, their voices of love and acceptance always present, remain a constant in my life. I am living my dream. My fairy tale doesn't end with the phrase: "and they lived happily ever after." It continues. I am not Cinderella waving from her carriage. The words "The End" will not dance across the screen. I am an eating disorder survivor, a social worker, a therapist, a wife, a mother, a sister, a daughter, and a friend. Oh, and I live in a larger body.

Nia Patterson

Eating Disorder and Mental Health Advocate

Host of Body Trauma Pod

I learned from a young age that "eating was bad." That it was okay to eat just the right amount but too much food or the wrong food and suddenly it became "bad." You were "bad." And you deserved what you got.

I cannot remember a single moment where someone pointed out that my body was bad or that I was bad for eating. But the feelings were there, and they clouded everything in shame. I do remember the doctor pulling out the BMI chart and pointing to the red area of being o*erweight, and later ob*se, but I don't think that was until 6th grade or middle school.

When I was younger I felt so much shame around eating and candy was one of my favorite things to eat so I hid it. In fact, I hid a lot of things when I was younger. But mainly, my candy routine consisted of eating it and then shoving the wrappers down into the back of the couch. Day after day. Week after week. Year after year. Until years later, when we finally moved houses and we moved the couch, my grandmother realized the back of it was filled with candy wrappers. Once everyone found my trash hoard the shame increased. I had to do better.

So, I started eating when I was away from home. In elementary school that meant when I walked to therapy once a week I would stop at the 7/11 on the way and I'd pick up snacks with the money my godmother had given me. My favorites were French onion Sun Chips, strawberry-kiwi Gatorade, and Juicy Fruit gum. I would take my snacks to therapy and eat them there. I would toss the wrappers on the way out and no one would know.

As I got older and subsequently fatter, I started sneaking more food. And when we moved and my godmother was no longer there to give me snacks and I didn't have a chance to walk by convenience stores after school I started to rely on only eating food at my friends' houses. I would have seconds and thirds of dinner at their houses. And I would drink sugary sodas in their basements. At a party at one of my friend's houses I ate so many starbursts I had a full-on sugar high and threw up in the bathroom. They never invited me over again.

I could not contain the high that food gave me. And my life then led me to boarding school for high school. I had gained so much weight in junior high that I was deeply ashamed of my body. I felt out of control around food and was scared. I wanted to shut it down and stop eating. I wanted to lose the weight and go back to being the thinner kid I was but puberty obviously made that impossible and the amount of food I was eating was leading to me gaining more weight.

I remember freshman year in high school my roommate was tiny and wore designer clothes, and I was fat and was barely able to fit in my closet to get dressed in the mornings. And so, I decided to go on another diet. To stop eating completely. I wanted people to notice that I had strong will-power and that I could discipline myself and lose the weight. It didn't work though. I didn't eat for a bit and when my roommate was out of the dorm I ordered Chinese food. About 2–3 meals and appetizers. My body was starving. But I was also so embarrassed that I wasn't able to discipline myself like I felt I wanted to. And I binged. I ate as much of the Chinese food as I could. And I was afraid my roommate would find out, so I hid the brown paper bag with food in it inside my closet. Two days later one of the other girls in the dorm found it. She sat me down in front of my roommate and explained that I couldn't just keep food sitting out in my room and not refrigerate it, and then eat it. She told me that I would get sick from it. I was so beyond ashamed. Not only was I eating food that had been sitting out and could make me sick but now everyone knew I could not keep it together long enough to lose weight. Everyone knew I was stuffing my face while they were gone.

The food hiding went on for years. When I had come home from boarding school, where I had no access to fast food, I would suddenly be able to drive down the street to any restaurant I wanted. And so I did. I would lie to my grandmother, take the car, go through a drive-through, and eat the food in the car alone. And when I came home, I would throw the food in the trash so that no one would know I was eating. I remember eating Taco Bell in the car with the windows down during a snowstorm so that the smell wouldn't linger in the car and because I had to have it and no one could know.

I hid the food I ate throughout high school and into college. And then after college as well. It was not until I started living on my own that I felt comfortable bringing food into my space and eating at home. But even now, years later, I often feel like I need to hide my food from the people around me. Frequently I do not advertise what I am eating unless it's "socially acceptable" food.

The fear of being fat and sloppy or fat and ravenous terrified me. I could not allow people to think that way about me. I had to be put together and willful and strong. I could not let people see me as "weak" or "gluttonous." Even though my body truly needed the food. And I was starving myself and still trying to deny myself food.

Being fat has affected how I eat for practically my whole life. It has kept me chained to secrets and shame. It has kept me eating in closets and cars and behind closed doors.

Fat liberation is the only way to freedom from that shame. I can speak about my shame to lessen it and stop engaging in the hiding behaviors to not make it taboo. But that does not lessen the societal pressure put on me to eat a certain way because of how my body looks. It also doesn't change my perceived health status because I am fat.

When you are thin and you eat a double double, it's considered cute and "fueling your body." When you are fat and you eat a double double, people stare at you from across the restaurant. They call you slurs and suggest diet plans. As if you do not know more about dieting than anyone else.

There will only be true freedom from the shame of eating while fat when fat liberation is realized and enforced. When the world accepts that fat people are not inherently unhealthy and that fat people deserve respect, love, and are worthy just like anyone else. Only then will the stigma be gone.

Shira Rose Rosenbluth, LCSW

Therapist

I was 10 years old when my eating disorder developed. I had started a Weight Watchers program for children just a few weeks earlier and that diet was the catalyst for my decades long battle with an eating disorder.

I remember having thoughts as far back as age 5 that my body was wrong, my body was bad, and that food was something to be ashamed of. I received the message that to be loved in my family, I needed to be thin and of course that message was only further solidified by our culture. The irony was that when I look back at photos of myself as a child, I wasn't particularly large until I was a teenager. And sometimes I wonder how differently things would've been if my body was left alone. But that diet was the flip that turned the switch on to my eating disorder and I spent the next two plus decades trying to claw my way out.

I was sent to a therapist at age 12 when my guidance counselor alerted my family that I needed help. I was scared but also relieved—maybe this therapist would know how to help me find some relief from the torment of my eating disorder and body hatred. Instead, my therapist looked my body up and down, raising her eyebrows as I shamefully told her that I was making myself vomit. "Oh okay, so you binge," she told me. I had finally told the truth about my eating disorder to a medical professional—and she ignored the fact that I was making myself throw up, because I didn't look like someone who would do that, or at least, not "successfully." My first therapist taught me something that would be reinforced over the next 21 years of my eating disorder: that restricting and purging are only concerning if you "look" like someone with an eating disorder, which in our culture usually means an emaciated white woman. And she confirmed my belief that my behaviors weren't all that problematic—what really mattered above all was making myself thin.

I continued seeing this eating disorder "expert" for two more years. My purging continued to escalate but I didn't bother bringing it up again. She suggested that I keep track of my intake with a food diary because she explained that it would show me just how much I was eating. When I didn't do that because everything about my eating felt overwhelmingly shameful and mortifying, she told me that it was clear that I didn't want to get better. She then told me to cut out every single food group besides protein because she believed it would stop me from bingeing. I know now that the more you restrict food groups, the likelier it will be that you'll feel more out of control around those foods. But as a child, I wasn't equipped with the knowledge I have now so I ended up feeling even more deeply ashamed that her advice caused me to spiral into an even deeper cycle of bingeing and purging, and I started to feel hopeless.

By the time I was 14, my purging had escalated so severely that my family could no longer deny it was happening. At my next therapy appointment, my mom reported this to the psychologist, who looked at me in shock and asked why I hadn't told her what was going on. I shrugged and mumbled an apology. I didn't know how to say that I had tried to tell her almost two years before—she just didn't believe me. But even though the therapist now believed I was purging, she continued to encourage restriction and reinforce the message that eating enough was optional because of the body I was in.

I was hospitalized for the first time with my eating disorder at age 14. On my second day, the doctor of the eating disorder ward congratulated me on losing weight overnight. "Look what happens when you don't binge and purge!" he told me. Once again, I was allowed to eat as little as I wanted because my body was different from the other patients on our floor. I then went to residential treatment where all the other patients had snacks besides me. My body was apparently too big for snacks.

In my early 20s, my eating disorder morphed into anorexia. My weight dropped dramatically and for the first time in my life, I fit in. I was able to shop for clothes anywhere I wanted, could eat publicly without raised eyebrows or judgement (though I was too scared to eat at that point), and was congratulated by everyone around me. It was a strange feeling to be praised over and over again for my anorexia while I was suffering so silently. I may have fit into our culture for the first time in my life, but it came at the expense of everything else. I couldn't travel because I was afraid of not being around my few safe foods, wouldn't go to holiday meals or any social events for fear of being around food, and spent my entire life dedicated to the pursuit of shrinking my body and needing to obey my eating disorder.

When I started seeing a treatment team that worked from a Health At Every Size® framework for the first time, they strongly insisted I go to treatment. I thought that maybe this was the time I'd finally be helped the way I needed but once again I was in for a huge disappointment. At first, I couldn't even get my insurance to cover any treatment at all because my BMI wasn't low enough. I was lucky enough to get a scholarship, but unfortunately I continued to experience weight stigma in treatment, as the treatment center was not Health At Every Size-informed. My thinner peers were encouraged to eat more and I was put on a maintenance meal plan. My appetite started to come back as I started eating and I was hungry all the time. My hunger caused me to obsess all day about food and I'd count the exchanges on my meal plan for hours every day, trying to figure out how to feel the most full with the exchanges I was allotted. It felt like every other diet I was forced to be on as a kid, down to needing to weigh and measure every morsel of food that entered my mouth, to the last ounce. The message that my body needed to be micromanaged and couldn't be trusted, was once again reinforced in treatment.

As someone who now treats eating disorders, I know that my body, regardless of the fact that it wasn't underweight according to BMI, was in fact underweight and needed more nourishment to heal after years of severe restriction. But instead, my therapist continued to tell me throughout treatment, "You haven't gained weight. Your body might just want to stay here. If you continue to follow your meal plan, maybe you won't gain the weight back." But I was hungry all the time. My eating disorder thoughts were constant and unbearable. My body was only at this weight because I starved myself there. And because the eating disorder noise was so intolerable, I ended up immediately turning to restriction again to quiet the noise when I went home. I ended up back in treatment just a few months later and I felt so ashamed. The staff would plate food for us and tell the other clients to eat 100% of the meal and then turn to me and say, "You eat 75%." We went out to get ice cream one day and they told everyone to get two scoops and then turned to me and told me to get a kiddie scoop. Once again, my body was wrong. Once again my body was different.

I eventually ended up turning to my Health At Every Size® colleagues for help because traditional eating disorder treatment had failed me for 15 years. For the first time in my life I was surrounded by people that accepted me as I am. They supported me with my meals for months in an environment where I felt completely safe in my body. My friends wanted me free of the eating disorder and knew it meant that my body would gain weight. Although I was scared of it, they weren't scared at all. They helped me fight my disorder on the days when it felt impossible to fight on my own. And I credit them with saving my life and helping me recover to a place of freedom from my eating disorder that I never imagined possible.

Everyone deserves eating disorder treatment that is free of stigma and fatphobia. People in ALL size bodies struggle with eating disorders and all deserve safe care. If you're struggling with an eating disorder in a body that isn't represented in the media, please know that your eating disorder is valid and you deserve respectful Health At Every Size® care. My own struggles have made me passionate about offering a safe space for my clients and on harder days, it's what keeps me in the fight. It's not just for me; it's for all of us.

Aaron Flores, RDN

Dietitian

Certified Body Trust Provider

I can remember the first time I realized that my body was a problem. I was about 15 years old, I was sitting in the car with my mom, and she suggested that I might want to see a dietitian, someone that she'd been working with, who could help me lose weight and eat healthier. Up until that point, I'd felt moments of discomfort around my body, mostly when I would go swimming or play sports, but it was never so intense that it caused any sort of worry for me at all. It felt like a mosquito buzzing around your ear...it happens quickly, startles you and your automatic instinct is to swat it away and that's what I did...I just swatted those feelings away. Up until that conversation in my mom's car, I'd gotten used to instinctively swatting away that pesky feeling of uneasiness in my body and would quickly move on to more important things.

As soon as my mom and I had that conversation though, I realized, "Hey, if she notices a problem, then my body must be something to worry about and to control." Looking back on it now, it was my entry point into diet culture. I'd seen my mom dieting many times. Going on and off diets. Rejoicing at her smaller body and shaming and putting down her larger one. From seeing her, I learned smaller bodies are to be praised and larger ones are to be shamed or rejected. With that in mind, off I went to see the dietitian.

I'd like to pause here and say, my mother meant no harm in her actions here. She was trying to do her best, raising a son as a single parent and doing everything she could to protect me from the world that judges larger bodies as less than. She had no idea the impact it would have later in my life. We've talked about it, made peace with this moment and I hold no anger towards her...as for diet culture, well that's another story, but we'll get there.

I go see this dietitian and let's be honest, I didn't do much of what she told me to do. Let's just say, I did very little of what she told me and I rode out the series of sessions, never really applying much of anything she said! But what I did apply "worked" and I did lose weight. From that I learned how intoxicating the praise I got was. All my family treated me differently and my friends did as well. It was a hugely visceral lesson that taught me that larger bodies are bad, smaller bodies are good.

That lesson stuck with me for quite some time. I went off to college and as many do, when there are no longer parents monitoring foods and left to our own devices, I gained weight. I also struggled in school. I am the person that would have benefited not just from a gap year, but probably a gap decade if that would have been an option. Eventually, I left school, came home back to LA and got a job working the tech industry during the Dot Com boom. It was good work, I got paid well and was mildly fulfilled but, my weight continued to go up and I was single.

The lesson of, "larger bodies bad, smaller bodies good" stuck with me and I knew, living in LA, the only way I was going to go on dates was to get smaller. (I know this is flawed thinking now, but at the time, it's what I believed 100%.) With this newfound drive, I remembered everything that dietitian taught me 10 years earlier and just like that I was off to the races. It was then that my true dieting behavior took hold and it was "working". I was militant about food and exercise. I avoided many food groups...I worked out to very specific goals and there was zero flexibility in any of it. As my weight went down, the praise and adoration soared...and so did my motivation to diet. Looking back at what I know now, I wish someone would have stepped in and told me there was a different way or that they were concerned, but a male, dieting and losing weight quickly is not something this society sees as disordered. I wonder if the same would have been true if my gender and body size were different?

There I was, dieting obsessively and socially, my life was great. But inside I was even more uncomfortable in my body. I had thin privilege but I felt like a larger man masquerading in a smaller body.

The other thing was that professionally, I was miserable. I was sick of this career in the tech world and that led me to think about finally going back to school for my degree, and what better career to choose when you are obsessed with food and losing weight? You guessed it, I wanted to be a dietitian. I went back to school and I dove headfirst into my education. and even though it seemed like a slow slog through numerous hurdles, in a matter of no time, I was a registered dietitian. At this time, my career goal was to help others lose weight, because I thought that was how you "fixed bodies". Slowly my career started to grow...yet my relationship with food stayed the same.

Internally, I was still tormented by food and my body. I was still dieting, counting calories, logging food and obsessed with every bite of food. There was no way in which I saw this as problematic and the reason is simple: diet culture is everywhere and has convinced everyone that eating "perfectly" with small portions and avoiding all unhealthy foods is not negotiable... you just do it. The other thing that it has us convinced of is this: many of the behaviors we see in dieting, are also seen in eating disorders. Did I have an eating disorder? I don't know. I was never officially diagnosed and I never went to treatment but I know now that I was totally disordered in my relationship with food.

As my career evolved, things didn't feel right. I felt like the sessions I was having with clients felt off. I felt their shame in coming to see me and no matter what I did, I could not figure out how to make them feel comfortable or safe in our meetings. It was this discomfort that motivated me to learn more and more about non-diet philosophies like Intuitive Eating, Health At Every Size® (HAES) and Body Trust®. It was these paradigms that helped bring me out of diet culture and change my personal and professional life forever. These things transformed my life, improved my relationship with food and sent my career in a totally different direction.

This period was really an unlearning of what I thought was right and true. I had to unlearn all that diet culture had taught me and I had to see the hard truth, I was full of internalized fatphobia and it had been tormenting me for years and my clients were suffering because of it. I was working in a space that was focused on weight loss and I slowly had to realize, by working this way, I was doing harm to people every day. As the unlearning continued, I started to see that weight and health are two separate things and the two are not as connected as we think they are.

Weight loss is the intervention de jour, no matter what ails you, losing weight will help. The unfortunate part of this idea is that weight loss, as an intervention, usually fails. Depending on what research you look at, anywhere from 75 to 95% of people regain weight after 5 years of stopping their diet. No matter which figure you choose, the truth is, the majority of people will regain weight after they stop dieting. It's not the individual's fault and no one is to blame, except the diet itself. I was no different and as I started to unravel how diet culture had controlled my life for years, my body began to recover and adapt to the routine of regular nourishment and more compassionate self-care. Has this unlearning meant my body has changed? Yes it has. Am I in a larger body today than I thought I would be? Yes, I am. Has this evolution led to me feeling more at home in this larger body than ever before? You better believe it.

How does that happen? How can living in a larger body mean more body acceptance than when I was smaller and strictly dieting? The answer might seem complex and unimaginable, but the reality is that it is so simple: the more you fight your body, the more it rebels against you. The more you try to control it, the less control you actually have. To embrace radical acceptance of your body, as it is today, is against every message we hear, but the strange thing is, it's where true self-care lies.

As men, and those who identify as men, body image is an area that has always felt taboo. It's ok for the locker room and it's ok when humor is involved but rarely is true space given to the struggle of body image and what is "acceptable" for men. The masculine ideal keeps men isolated and afraid to express any emotions, because to do so is weak, unsafe and a sign of weakness. Yet, many men are struggling, they just never get to say it. Having run a series of body image groups for men, the most unifying theme that comes up is, "I wish I'd been able to talk about this with my friends earlier." Instead, men, and those identifying as men, sit in silence, assuming their suffering is just their own, without any community to share and ultimately heal. This is how the patriarchy affects men. It is the unspoken message that our bodies are our own to deal with. Don't express any feelings around it, just work on making it more muscular or thinner. But don't show feelings around it, because that is a sign of weakness and that will not be tolerated.

When I look back on my experience and how diet culture affected me and my body, there is a sense of anger that shows up. I'm angry that there is so much pressure on all of us to have a body that "fits" and if we don't we are less than. I'm angry that the female body is so highly scrutinized. I'm angry at how whiteness and white supremacy are so entwined with diet culture and how that affects people of color. I'm angry that men don't have space to struggle with this. This anger though is not in a vacuum and it's what fuels me everyday. It's fuel to use my voice to speak up against diet culture. It fuels me to challenge long-held narratives around bodies and health. It fuels me to fight against fatphobia. It fuels me to be vulnerable to the world and say, I'm a man in a fat body. I accept my body. I care for my body. My body is mine and not yours. I choose how to nourish and treat my body. I choose respect over hate because hating my body is what started me down this road in the first place. My body is a place for peace, kindness, compassion and love! Yours can be too.

Kaitlin Anderle, MSW

Therapist

My journey to fat positivity was paved with fatphobia, weight bias, diet culture, and an eating disorder that went undiagnosed for a long time. Let me bring you to the beginning of this bumpy and unexpected journey when I thought I was making a decision that would change the path my life took, which it did, just not in the way I thought it would. I was 22 years old, and I thought I was making the most positive and healthy choice I had ever made up to that point. I thought I was taking control of my life, and I was going to finally have the life I truly wanted; I was going to have weight loss surgery.

I had considered weight loss surgery prior, but it was a conversation with my mom that solidified the thought into a plan. I have had a complicated relationship with my mom for a long time; however, one aspect of our relationship I thought I had figured out was that my mom accepted my appearance. In fact, she was the one person in my family who never commented on my weight or body size growing up. So, I was stunned when my mom brought up the idea of weight loss surgery. When I was surprised by this, she explained that she often would cry to people and say, "If Kaitlin is okay with what she sees when she looks in the mirror, then I guess that is all that matters, even if it hurts me."

It wasn't the one comment alone; it was a lifetime of feeling invisible and too visible at the same time. It was all of the fatphobia I had experienced throughout my life that led me to believe that unless I changed my body size, no one would ever truly see me for me. I genuinely thought that I was having weight loss surgery with only health and good intentions. In reality, I knew that the operation would permanently impose a physical restriction on my food intake, and that was what I wanted. I had already been imposing food restrictions on myself for years. I deprived myself of food as my apology for existing in a fat body, and if I did eat, purging was my penance.

I had the vertical sleeve gastrectomy surgery in the summer of 2013, and barely anyone knew I was having the surgery due to the shame I felt surrounding getting the surgery. The recovery was worse and far more painful than I had anticipated, despite not having any major complications. I was told that I would be able to go back to my regular activity after two days. Two days after the surgery I was miserable. I could barely keep water down, but I was okay with that because I obsessively weighed myself, and I was losing weight. Fast forward a few weeks and people started to notice my weight loss, and within a few months people who had hardly spoken to me before were telling me I was an inspiration.

I posted before and after pictures and eventually shared about my surgery because I was getting so many messages asking how I did it. On social media it appeared that I was the happiest I had ever been. In reality, I had never felt more alone, empty, and disconnected from myself. My counselor at the time referred me to a dietitian after I began to share my thoughts surrounding food and my body. It was then that my road began to take a different course.

I began meeting with a dietitian who introduced me to Health at Every Size and intuitive eating; this information provided me with a perspective I had never heard. Over time, I was able to acknowledge that I had an eating disorder. Still, it wasn't until I began seeing my current counselor who specializes in treating eating disorders that I realized the connection between my eating disorder and my weight loss surgery. During one of our sessions, I explained that I had no problem talking about my eating disorder recovery, but I struggled to talk about my weight loss surgery. She asked, "why do you see your eating disorder and your weight loss surgery separately?" She was right; they are not separate. Having weight loss surgery was the most radical manifestation of my eating disorder.

It was my eating disorder voice that told me having 80% of my stomach removed would solve 100% of my problems. I began sharing my journey of eating disorder recovery on Instagram this past summer, seven years after I had my surgery. My story is not unique, but I think many people with similar stories are silenced by shame if they have regained some, all, or more weight after weight loss surgery. There are endless before and after pictures, but so few people sharing about the risks surrounding weight loss surgery. Informed consent does not exist without being fully informed. The reality is that many people will regain the weight they might have lost after weight loss surgery. I can only speak to my experience, and I did regain probably all of the weight that I had lost, but I wouldn't know though because I don't own a scale anymore.

References

Fletcher, D. (2009). The fat acceptance movement. Time Magazine. http://content.time.com/time/nation/article/0,8599,1913858,00.html

Puhl, R. & Heuer, C. (2010). Obesity stigma: important considerations for public health. *American Journal of Public Health*, 100(6): 1019–1028.

9 Trauma

Taking Back Your Power

There is one topic that we have found tends to be overlooked in nearly every discussion about eating disorders – and that topic is trauma. It is all well and good for us to tell you to "change your behaviors, change your life." But the fact is, trauma is a huge underlying factor for a lot of us with eating disorders. And we can't *truly* be expected to heal until we address this. To understand what this means, you will first need to understand what the hell we mean when we say "trauma."

The term "trauma" is kind of misunderstood. Back in the day, trauma was a term thrown around in psychology land that tended to go hand in hand with a diagnosis of Post Traumatic Stress Disorder (PTSD). PTSD was a disorder that was added to the DSM in 1980. Basically, PTSD is a disorder that involves witnessing or being involved in a catastrophic stressor – one that causes much higher levels than typical painful human experiences. After witnessing said event, someone with PTSD would then start to experience symptoms such as nightmares, avoidance of certain situations that remind the person of the trauma, flashbacks, and anxiety (American Psychiatric Association, 2013).

BUT – in the past 40 years, the field of psychology has pretty much re-vamped our understanding of trauma. Psychologists are no longer viewing trauma as a dichotomous diagnosis (dichotomous means you either have it, or ya don't). Trauma is now viewed as existing on a continuum (Scaer, 2005). This suggests that events no longer have to be catastrophic or life-threatening to cause a trauma reaction. If it helps, try conceptualizing trauma like a cut – sometimes we can get minor cuts, right? They hurt when they happen, but our body can usually heal them pretty quickly. Other cuts are larger – they take a lot of time to heal, and also likely need some outside medical attention. (Anyone ever had stiches as a kid? *shudder*) The point is, those big cuts can heal too – they just likely take more time, need more attention, and may or may not leave a scar. It is also important to note that sometimes the small cuts can get infected and turn into bigger cuts. Maybe they weren't cleaned out well enough initially. Maybe your immune system was suppressed when you got the small cut. Whatever the reason, that small nick has now turned into a huge pain in the you-know-what – and it is going to need some medical attention – STAT.

Continuum of Trauma

trauma	Trauma	TRAUMA

Figure 9.1 Continuum of Trauma

You feel us with this cut metaphor? Trauma is similar. It is a psychological reaction to a stressful event. The event does **not** have to be life-threatening or even initially terrifying. It just has to be something that causes you stress and overwhelms your nervous system's ability to cope. That's it folks. With this in mind, the idea is that there is a continuum of trauma, and that we *all* experience events that fall somewhere on that continuum (Figure 9.1). Check it out:

When picturing this trauma continuum, we find it helpful to chunk traumas into two main groups: trauma with a small t, and Trauma with a big T.

Small-t traumas are life events that are seriously distressing, but not life-threatening or body-integrity-threatening. We want to point out though that they can still be incredibly impactful! Examples of small-t traumas are: bullying, divorce, relocation, financial issues, legal issues, and harassment. These small-t traumas can also be deeply specific, and not super obvious. Some examples of subtle small-t traumas that we have experienced? Going to a psychiatric hospital, witnessing our parents experience the death of their parents, infertility, consistently being told that a parent likes our sibling better, and the list goes on. You see, small-t traumas are frequent and personal. They are events or experiences that leave a negative emotional impact. It is important to note that repeated or chronic small-t traumas can add up and eventually move down that continuum into big-T Trauma territory.

Take a moment to list out the small-t traumas that you have experienced in your life:

_____

_____

_____

_____

_____

Big-T Traumas are the more obvious types of trauma. They may be what you automatically think of when the word "trauma" is thrown out. Big-T Trauma is inherently extraordinary and can often be life-threatening. These are events that often threaten our body integrity. People often report experiencing a feeling of helplessness as these types of trauma occur. Examples of big-T Traumas are: sexual assault, car accidents, overdosing, suicide attempts, natural disasters, miscarriages, war, etc. People tend to experience avoidance more obviously and abruptly with these types of traumas. They are more identifiable than the small-t traumas. In fact, you probably already know if you have experienced a big-T Trauma.

A Word on Systemic Trauma: Systemic trauma refers to the features of our environment, institutions, and overall culture that both cause trauma, and maintain it. Racism is a prime example of systemic trauma. Because our culture is steeped in white supremacy, racism is threaded throughout most aspects of our environment. Schools, religious institutions, jobs, universities, sports, hospitals, prisons, the media, our beauty ideals – all uphold white supremacy and contribute to the oppression of Black and brown folks in various ways. Other examples of systemic trauma are homophobia and the heteronormative expectation, transphobia, fatphobia, and sexism. Systemic trauma is most certainly big-T Trauma. It is chronic and insidious. This is why eating disorder advocacy must center the voices of the most marginalized people at all times.

Colleen

I have dealt with several big-T Traumas in my life. My small-t traumas have ranged wildly from bullying, to feeling like an outcast at times in my own family, to infertility, and on and on and on. I used to assume that big-T Trauma was more important than the small-t trauma in terms of what "caused" my eating disorder. But the truth is – these are *all* important. Yes, my big-T Traumas kick-started my desire to take up less space and appear less like a sexual being, but the desire was planted years prior, throughout all of those small-t traumas. A thousand papercuts can become infected and hurt just as badly as one giant gash.

Take a moment to fill out your own personal trauma continuum (Figure 9.2) with any small-t and big-T Traumas that you have experienced. Cluster the small-t traumas around the left end, and the big-T Traumas around the middle. At the far right, underneath the uppercase TRAUMA, write down

Figure 9.2 Continuum of Trauma

any of the small-t or big-T traumas that you believe are not healed/still impact you negatively today.

So – you have now taken some time to identify your own traumas, and their potential impact. You might be thinking, "this is all well and good, but what the hell does it have to do with my eating disorder?" In a word – everything. Studies have shown that people who have experienced trauma (big-T Trauma that is), are more likely to be diagnosed with an eating disorder later in life (Brewerton, 2008). In fact, one study found that 74% of women attending residential treatment indicated that they had experienced a significant trauma (Gleaves et al., 1998). Seventy-four percent! That is ¾ of the women in that treatment center – a *huge majority.* This actually makes a ton of sense when you break it down. Trauma (especially that big-T kind) tends to involve a feeling of extreme helplessness – whether it is from abuse (of any kind), a natural disaster, a car accident – that shitty feeling of being out of control and helpless tends to be universal. If the trauma has a lasting psychological impact, that feeling of helplessness starts to haunt us. And what do we do when a bad feeling is haunting us? *We find a way to cope.*

We wish we could say that the majority of humans find healthy ways to cope. But the truth is, a lot of us (hi, hello from both of your authors) stumble into coping skills that may not necessary be healthy, *but they work.* Take drug abuse for example – some people may begin to experiment with drugs as a way to numb some sort of icky feeling. Is drug abuse healthy? Naw. Does it work to help us numb our feelings? Hell yes – at least moment- arily. Self-harm is another great example. Is it healthy? Of course not. Does it work? Again – hell to the yes. (Hi friends! Colleen here – I want to take a moment to acknowledge the fact that I utilized self-harm for many years, and can absolutely speak to the fact that it momentarily does provide a quick numbing form of relief. Let's remove the shame when it comes to talking about the various ways that we used to cope with emotional pain.) Do these things work long term in helping us move forward? Of course not!

Now, with this in mind, consider disordered eating. Similar to both drug abuse and self-harm, disordered eating can help us to cope in the short term. Many of us stumble into using it as a coping skill. We, for example, never realized that the restriction involved in a simple diet would aid in allowing us to numb our memories of sexual trauma or bullying. But that's what restriction does, right? It allows us to numb our feelings. Avoiding food is a fantastic (sarcasm people) way to hyper-focus on a goal, so that your mind has no room to think about the dark stuff. Bingeing and purging allows us to disconnect from our minds, and our sucky reality – if only for a few moments.

Essentially, if you have suffered from a big-T Trauma, or a bunch of accumulated small-t traumas, you may have stumbled into using eating disordered behaviors to distract yourself from this. The eating disorder, you see, has been super functional in this regard. It has helped you to cope with some seriously dark shit. You can thank your eating disorder – yes, thank it – for helping you to survive the past. You are not weak. You are a resilient damn survivor.

Jennifer

I am a survivor of sexual trauma including sexual assault (big-T Trauma) as well as some other smaller-t traumas including feeling like an outcast in high school, and so on. At my core, being a survivor of trauma impacted my sense of self and my self-worth. I blamed myself and my body for what had happened to me and this led to feelings of worthlessness and ugliness. I also struggled with issues around needing to feel in control after what had happened. For a while, I fixated on trying to get the best grades possible, and then that need to have something to obsess over and control turned to food and my body. Of course my eating disorder was more complex than that – however, I do feel that my experience of trauma contributed to the perfect storm that caused it to develop. I also developed PTSD as a result of the trauma that I experienced, which took me completely by surprise as I had a lot of misconceptions about PTSD. I associated it with soldiers that had been through combat and thought that, to struggle with PTSD, I had to have constant nightmares or become jumpy at loud noises. I personally struggled with dissociation, suicidality related to trauma reminders, difficulty with intimacy, and a variety of other symptoms. Being able to find healing from both the eating disorder and PTSD has been incredibly freeing.

Journaling Prompt

What would I be thinking about if I wasn't using up my cognitive energy to focus on food and weight? What from my past or present might I be avoiding by focusing on food and weight? (Identifying these things will be helpful in pointing you in the direction of your own trauma that needs and deserves attention.)

A Word on Sexual Trauma

Sexual trauma is an absolute nightmare. *No one* should ever be subjected to someone else using and abusing your body. When it comes to eating disorders, sexual trauma has a very specific and complicated link – so complicated, that we felt it was important to speak specifically to this experience.

When we say sexual trauma, we are referring to experiences of sexual assault and/or rape. We are *not* solely referring to penetrative rape. This is super important, because often times our clients experience shame at having trauma symptoms in response to sexual assault that is not penetrative rape. We are here to say – sexual trauma can stem from rape, sexual abuse, stalking, sexual harassment, street harassment, childhood sexual abuse, familial sexual abuse or incest, sex trafficking, online sexual harassment, and sexual violence in relationships. It is an umbrella term, and there is no one "worst" type of sexual trauma.

Sexual trauma involves a violation that occurs *to your body.* Essentially, when we experience sexual trauma, our brains are sent a very concrete and terrifying message: *my body is not safe.* Because, as we've talked about here, our bodies are our homes, that message translates to: *the home that I reside in 24-7 is not safe.* These profound violations to our body can lead to a desire to dissociate from our body. Why? Because if your body is not a safe place to reside – if it can be violated by another in such a terrifying way – then it makes sense that you would want to escape it. This danger message can also lead to feelings of powerlessness, worthlessness, objectification, and feelings of being "dirty." The best way to escape that our subconscious can often come up with is by *controlling.* For some of us, this controlling can manifest as restriction, bingeing, or purging.

So, you see, there is so much to unpack when it comes to each of our own trauma continuums. When it comes to healing from your eating disorder, the most important step to take in terms of your own trauma is just that – the unpacking of the trauma.

Trauma grows in secrecy and shame. The best antidote is sharing and processing. This is why we *highly* recommend seeking out a trained therapist to talk about this stuff. As we've been saying all along, we recommend the guidance of a therapist for the entire recovery process – but this guidance is perhaps most crucial when it comes to healing from trauma.

Steps to Taking Back Your Power

Self-exploration: You'll want to begin asking yourself: How is my relationship with food similar to how I am relating to others? How am I using food or my body to communicate my pain that feels unspeakable? Am I taking out misdirected anger/powerlessness on my body?

Therapy: This is a biggie my friends. Therapy is a game changer when it comes to trauma.

Internalize self-compassion: Ya gotta. Ya just gotta. Work to cultivate some compassion for yourself at whatever age the trauma occurred. This can involve imagining what you would say to yourself as an adult, or simply thinking of how you might have compassion for anyone else who has experienced a similar trauma. Another exercise to use in this area would be writing a letter to your younger self, expressing compassion and love.

Body work: Trauma often involves a disconnect from your body. You can come to almost "vote your body off the island" so to speak, and learn to exist mostly in your mind and/or emotions. Body work is a way to come home to your body. It is essentially merging your body, mind, and soul into one beautiful triad. Body work can include things like yoga, massage therapy, and movement therapy. But it can also be less formal than that. Body work can be as simple as an intentional mindfulness practice in which you notice different sensations in your body for five minutes each day.

Journaling Prompt

Write a thank you letter to your eating disorder.

Say whaaaat? That's right. We want you to write out a thank you letter to your eating disorder for helping you cope with whatever small-t and big-T traumas have occurred in your life. Make sure to include that you no longer require your eating disorder's services. Kind of like a "thank you for trying to help, but I'm going to try something different now" letter.

References

American Psychiatric Association (2013). *Diagnostic and Statistical Manual of Mental Disorders*, Fifth Edition. Arlington, VA.

Brewerton, T.D. (2008). The links between PTSD and eating disorders. *Psychiatric Times*, 25(6): 1–7.

Gleaves, D.H., Eberenz, K.P., & May, M.C. (1998). Scope and significance of post-traumatic symptomatology among women hospitalized for an eating disorder. *International Journal of Eating Disorders*, 24: 147–156.

Scaer, R. (2005). *The Trauma Spectrum: Hidden Wounds and Human Resiliency*. New York: W.W. Norton and Company.

10 Orthorexia

The Eating Disorder That Hides in Plain Sight

Picture this – you've suddenly developed an interest in "healthy eating." Your Instagram feed is filled with beautifully styled Açaí bowls and colorful salads. You're trying to eat in a way that is as "pure" and "healthy" as possible – and have even started making your own almond milk! Waking up each day to milk those almonds is tiring, but you push through. (What? We think we're funny, ok?) Your friends praise you for your "dedication" and devotion to wellness.

What they don't know is that your brain is becoming increasingly occupied with thoughts about food. They don't see the terrible anxiety that you face when asked to go out to eat. In fact, realistically, this focus on "wellness" is causing you to be physically and mentally unwell.

If this is you, if you relate to this scenario at all, you may just be struggling with an eating disorder that often hides in plain sight: orthorexia.

Orthorexia nervosa is an eating disorder (not yet officially recognized, but seen as on the rise by many professionals) that sneaks into your life disguised as a search for "health" and "wellness." Essentially, orthorexia is when someone's fixation on what they deem to be "healthy eating" becomes an unhealthy obsession (we've both been here and it blows!) ("Orthorexia," n.d.).

Our culture has an unhealthy fixation on this idea of "wellness." Diets are generally seen as passé – so diet culture has gotten even more crafty in terms of marketing. Now, "wellness culture" (we're looking at you juice cleanses and "clean eating!") has become trendier than more traditional forms of dieting. Certain foods have been labeled as "superfoods" in another brilliant marketing attempt – and even restaurants like Panera have jumped on the "clean eating" marketing bandwagon.

> **Colleen**
>
> Orthorexia snuck up on me like no other eating disorder presentation I've ever had before. It was like wading into a small pool of water, and then suddenly realizing I had been swept away in a tidal wave. My middle school, high school, and college eating disorder presented

itself a little more…shall we say…blatantly? I knew for the most part that what I was doing was unhealthy. I knew that my eating was an absolute shit show. I knew that I wanted to appear sickly thin. But this orthorexia phase was different. I started out wanting to "clean up my eating" in graduate school. I preached to others about my newfound way of life – about how I had left the laxatives and restricting in the past – about how I had finally "come home to myself" in terms of my relationship with food (*cue eye roll*; it's ok – you can roll yours eyes at grad school, Colleen). In retrospect it was clear what was happening – I was scared, lonely, and sad in graduate school and needed something to cling onto to give me some semblance of control. If you relate to this – if your eating disorder has shifted to this sneaky presentation of "the chase for perfect health" over time, please know that there is nothing to be ashamed of. You, like me, have been bamboozled by wellness culture my friend. It happens to the best of us. Now it's time to clap back to orthorexia – onwards and upwards!

The term "wellness" was first popularized by Dr. Halbert Dunn in the 1950s. From the 1980s until the 2000s, the wellness movement began to pick up steam – until it became the mega industry that it is today (Global Wellness Institute, n.d.).

Then, celebrities like Dr. Oz became champions of the "wellness" movement. This cultural fixation continued to gain momentum as workplaces created "workplace wellness programs," and fitness facilities experienced a ton of growth (Global Wellness Institute, n.d.). Soon after, "wellness" became a buzzword and there were lots of products and services marketing themselves under this umbrella.

In 2015, the wellness industry around the world was valued at $3.7 trillion (Blei, 2017). It makes sense in today's cultural climate that orthorexia nervosa is an emerging eating disorder, because *so* many of the behaviors that someone might demonstrate are socially sanctioned and praised.

So how do you know if you might be struggling with orthorexia?

Some of the warning signs include the following:

- Interest and preoccupation with what the person deems as "healthy eating."
- Cutting out certain food groups (i.e. carbs, fat, sugar), which often becomes increasingly restrictive over time.
- Food rules, i.e. "I only eat bread that's whole wheat" and eating a small range of foods.
- Rigidity and lack of flexibility around food-intense guilt if food rules are "broken."
- Thinking about food in terms of morality and purity.

- Spending hours reading nutrition articles online, reading recipes, thinking about "healthy eating."
- Anxiety around events, eating at restaurants, eating at social settings, etc.

("Orthorezia," n.d.).

List out any of the warning signs that resonate with you:

What's the Difference Between "Healthy Eating" and Orthorexia?

First off – we define "healthy eating" as eating enough food for your bod, eating a wide variety of foods, and eating foods that you enjoy. Unfortunately, diet culture defines "healthy eating" differently. However, what's the difference between someone who really likes kale and someone struggling with orthorexia? Honestly? A lot of it comes down to level of flexibility and the intention behind eating certain foods.

For instance, two people could have the same action: ordering a soup and salad, however we have to look at the intention behind this decision. One person might be ordering the salad because they feel guilty ordering anything else – and their eating disorder tells them this is the "healthiest" option. Another person might tune into what they are craving and notice that the salad looks really delicious. Other times this same person might tune in and crave a burger, tacos, or a wrap and they can order these things guilt-free. This example depicts the same action: but one is eating disorder-driven and the other isn't.

Another important distinction is looking at flexibility. Someone might have certain foods that they enjoy, but they are going to a dinner party where different foods will be served, and they are able to be flexible without shame, guilt, or anxiety. For someone with orthorexia, often there is much more rigidity around eating and they might choose to skip the dinner party, bring their own food, or eat the other food with intense feelings of anxiety and guilt.

The bottom line here is that orthorexia is not simply a preference towards eating in a certain way, it's a serious mental illness that can be detrimental mentally and physically (Bratman, 2017).

Jennifer

My eating disorder started out as orthorexia and then later morphed. In the beginning, I truly believed that I was "being healthy." I posted pictures on social media of colorful fruit bowls and everyone praised me for the way that I was eating. Initially, I didn't realize that I had a problem because my behaviors were SO socially acceptable. From the outside I looked like someone who was "health conscious" or eating in a way that society (cough *diet culture* cough) deems to be "good." No one knew that I was secretly becoming terrified of certain foods. No one knew that I once watched someone eat a muffin and thought to myself, "I wouldn't eat that even if someone paid me tons of money." (Note: now I eat muffins whenever I want to!) No one knew that I was obsessed with cooking foods that I wouldn't eat myself – and that the range of foods that I deemed "acceptable" was getting more and more narrow. My eating disorder was hidden in plain sight.

Lies Orthorexia May Tell You

Orthorexia (like other eating disorders) tells a lot of lies. So, we're here to do some (what else?) debunking. The following are some common lies orthorexia may tell you, and our retorts.

1. There is nothing wrong with wanting to "eat healthy."

Orthorexia is a sneaky eating disorder that hides under the guise of "health and wellness." While this one might appear more socially acceptable it's just as soul-sucking and harmful as the other eating disorders. Being rigid with what you are eating, lacking flexibility, cutting out food groups, having anxiety/guilt/shame around food, and being ruled by an eating disorder voice in your head is NOT mentally or physically healthy.

2. If I add a variety of foods back into my diet, I will become "unhealthy."

Health is person and context specific. For instance, if we are trying to power through a long afternoon of seeing clients, which snack option would be the healthier choice in that moment: a plate of steamed broccoli or a bag of chips?

Put your best guess here _____

The plate of steamed broccoli would not be likely to hold either of us over through our afternoons. But the chips – well those provide carbs and fat, which would have more staying power to power us onward.

A wide range of foods can be part of a healthy diet. Barring a diagnosed medical concern, ALL foods can fit into a healthy diet. Also, research suggests that adding a wide variety of foods for those in eating disorder recovery actually leads to better outcomes (Schebendach et al., 2011; Latner & Wilson, 2000).

3.   If I work to recover from orthorexia, I will lose "control."

Orthorexia might tell you that you are "in control" because you are controlling what you are putting into your body. But, when you are avoiding social events, having to analyze nutrition labels, and feeling intense anxiety, guilt, and shame over food – who is actually in control? (spoiler alert: it's not you!)

Truth bomb: the deeper ya get into an eating disorder the less "in control" you actually are.

Challenges of Orthorexia Recovery

The first big obstacle is just recognizing that you have a problem (we know this was initially an issue for us!).

Recovering from orthorexia might feel like you are going against every cultural norm (and to be frank, you may be). And for real – we KNOW it's freaking hard to work on recovery when everyone around you is talking about the so-called "o*esity" epidemic, their latest juice cleanse, and their "clean eating plan." Living in a world where we are all fish swimming in "diet culture water" can make recovery from orthorexia challenging.

Another tough thing can be the social praise that you might have received around your eating patterns (and the social praise that you may have received if any weight loss occurred). But it's important to remember that many people are swimming in this same "diet culture water" and their praise is just a mirror into the issues that they might be struggling with.

People who truly love and care about you will not love you any less once you are able to let go of rigid eating patterns. If anything, recovery will open up your life even more to where you can better engage in relationships.

How to Dig Yourself Out

1.   Seek help.

Listen up ya'll: getting professional help is SO important. No one should have to try to recover alone. This is why the first thing we encourage you to do is to reach out to a local eating disorder therapist who can do an assessment. From there, you can look at building a treatment team to potentially include a dietitian, psychiatrist, physician, recovery coach, and/ or a group.

2. *Cultivate an awareness of the ways in which orthorexia is impacting your life.*

Another important first step is to start to pay attention to the ways in which orthorexia might be impacting your life.

Start by being mindful (i.e. curious without judgment) about the thoughts and behaviors that you are experiencing (Mindful Staff, 2020). Rather than judging or beating yourself up for the symptoms that you are exhibiting, practice simply observing them. Before we can change thoughts and behaviors we have to start with a solid awareness of them.

3. *Fear food hierarchy.*

Create a hierarchy of foods that you have anxiety, guilt/shame around (starting with the least anxiety-provoking to the most anxiety-provoking. We like to use a 1–10 scale). Then, next to each food write the orthorexia inspired thoughts around the food. Gradually work your way through the hierarchy – ideally with a support person (i.e. therapist, friend, spouse). Make sure that you repeat each food until the fear goes away.

4. *Surround yourself with pro-recovery inspiration and remove any content that keeps you stuck.*

Are you following people on social media who strengthen your recovery or weaken it? May we kindly suggest that you unfollow anyone who makes you feel badly about your body or food choices? (ahem – fitspo and "wellness" accounts). Then, it's important to add in some pro-recovery, Health At Every Size®, and non-diet accounts (you know, things that invoke joy and positive inspiration).

What we surround ourselves with can have a big impact on us. So, it's crucial to start to surround yourself with pro-recovery messaging and take out anything that fuels the orthorexia thinking patterns.

5. *Work to redefine what "health" means to you.*

Society's definition of "health" is often super misguided. First off, it's important to note that there are plenty of people who struggle with chronic illnesses who will never be "healthy." Someone's health status is NOT a determinant of their worth or value. Society loves to overemphasize food and movement when it comes to health – however, these things are really just a drop in the bucket when it comes to the big picture of health.

It's crucial to expand our definition of health to include mental health, emotional health, and the health of our relationships. For instance, someone with orthorexia might start avoiding social settings to stay home eating their so-called "health foods." However, going to the social gathering and eating the food that's served there is actually *far healthier.*

The Harvard Gazette did an 80-year study looking at mortality and factors that were involved. They discovered that the biggest predictor of living a long life was relationships and relationship satisfaction (Mineo, 2017). When someone is struggling with an eating disorder it often becomes their primary relationship, to the detriment of other relationships. So, it's important to remember that through the recovery process you are actually becoming *healthier* (in a variety of different ways!).

It's also important to note that there are other factors which play into health, such as socioeconomic status (SES), which has been found to be one of the big predictors of mortality. However, SES is not often talked about when it comes to health outcomes ("The Lancet," 2017). Why? Well, our guess is that there is not much money to be made off of research about SES and mortality. (Damn capitalism.) Those of a lower socioeconomic status might not have access to medical care or quality medical care. Additionally, high stress levels (hello cortisol – the stress hormone) associated with juggling multiple jobs and/or having financial stress could play into more adverse health outcomes ("The Lancet," 2017).

Quick! Come up with your own definition of what it means for you to "be healthy" that is separate from orthorexia's definition:

An example: Healthy for me means: engaging in meaningful relationships, taking care of my mental and physical health (i.e. going to those dentist appts that I don't wanna go to!), and nourishing my soul.

Now that you have your personal definition of health, try this: Under the following categories, list things that you currently do, as well as things that you can add in, to enhance your health. The catch? These things should have NOTHING to do with food and exercise.

1. *Mental Health*

2. *Physical Health*

3. *Health of Relationships*

4. *Emotional Health*

5. *Spiritual Health (**if applicable)*

Journaling Prompts

1. What do you think you're really searching for in this "pursuit of health?" (ex: a smaller body, a sense of "control")
2. How does your eating disorder define "health"?
3. What would be a more pro-recovery definition of "health"?
4. What are the functions that orthorexia is currently serving in your life? (i.e. makes me feel safe)
5. What are the ways in which orthorexia is negatively impacting your life?
6. What are some more values-aligning ways that you could get some of the adaptive functions met (i.e. for feelings of safety doing a safe space visualization or spending time with people you feel safe around)?
7. List two orthorexia rules that you can challenge over the next few weeks.

References

Blei, D. (2017 Jan. 4). The false promises of wellness culture. *JSTOR Daily*. https://daily.jstor.org/the-false-promises-of-wellness-culture/

Bratman, S. (2017, June 8). The authorized Bratman orthorexia self-test. www.orthorexia.com/the-authorized-bratman-orthorexia-self-test/

Global Wellness Institute (n.d.) History of wellness. https://globalwellnessinstitute.org/industry-research/history-of-wellness/

Latner, J.D. & Wilson, G.T. (2000, Sept.). Cognitive-behavioral therapy and nutritional counseling in the treatment of bulimia nervosa and binge eating. *Eating Behaviors*, *1*(1): 3–21. https://doi.org/10.1016/s1471-0153(00)00008-8

Mindful Staff. (2020, July 8). What is mindfulness? Mindful. www.mindful.org/what-is-mindfulness/

Mineo, L. (2017, April 11). Good genes are nice, but joy is better. The Harvard Gazette. https://news.harvard.edu/gazette/story/2017/04/over-nearly-80-years-harvard-study-has-been-showing-how-to-live-a-healthy-and-happy-life/

Orthorexia (n.d). National Eating Disorders Association. www.nationaleatingdisorders.org/learn/by-eating-disorder/other/orthorexia

Schebendach, J.E., Mayer, L.E., Devlin, M.J., Attia, E., Contento, I.R., Wolf, R.L., & Walsh, B.T. (2011, May). Food choice and diet variety in weight-restored patients with anorexia nervosa. *Journal of the American Dietetic Association*, *111*(5): 732–736. doi: 10.1016/j.jada.2011.02.002

The Lancet. (2017, January 31). Low socioeconomic status reduces life expectancy and should be counted as a major risk factor in health policy, study says. *ScienceDaily*. Retrieved June 3, 2020 from www.sciencedaily.com/releases/2017/01/170131190102.htm

11 Getting Unstuck
The Trap of Partial Recovery

Let's be real here: partial recovery can feel like both an intoxicating and exhausting place to be. Partial recovery is a wasteland between totally caught in an eating disorder and fully recovered. For many, this encapsulates the "middle stages of recovery" and it's an easy place to get stuck. We know. We've been there. But we managed to get ourselves unstuck. And we've helped many clients to get unstuck too.

So how do you know if you're caught in the trap of partial recovery? Do any of these statements feel familiar?

- I've challenged some of my eating disorder behaviors and feel generally more "functional" but I still hold onto some of my safe "rules."
- I tell myself that this is "as good as it gets" in terms of recovery and that I'll just have to settle here.
- I've let go of a lot of my food rules – but still have a rigid exercise routine.
- I have a lot more freedom than I had at the lowest point of my eating disorder – but I still have moments where I feel pretty trapped.
- I am not completely free and flexible with food and my relationship to movement.
- I have traded some of my eating disorder behaviors for more "socially acceptable" eating disorder behaviors (i.e. getting "really into" fitness, "eating clean," focusing on "wellness" when it comes to food).
- If I really admit it to myself, I am still engaging in behaviors to try to micromanage my weight.
  **Add checkmarks next to the statements that resonate with you

Partial recovery is when you have let go of some of your eating disorder behaviors, but are still keeping some in your back pocket. It is like being in a bigger cage then you were caught in before. You have more room to move around. Things feel more comfortable. But you're still confined by the walls around you. Being what we like to call "in strong recovery" or "full recovery" recovered is when there is no longer a cage at all.

Colleen

Oh friends. No shame if you are stuck in partial recovery. I chilled in partial recovery land for YEARS. I didn't always know it, but I did. I remember telling my boyfriend (now my husband) "This is just as good as it is going to get for me. I am always going to be a person who NEEDS to get to the gym. I will always be a little weird around pizza." I would also repeatedly tell anyone who was interested, "but it is WORLDS better than where I was before." "This is full recovery to me," I would say. "Having a good relationship with food and my body – that's not personally possible. Best I can hope is to not abuse and slowly destroy my body."

This is another one of those things that took becoming radically honest with myself to change. I had to pony up to the truth that I was telling myself "this is as good as it gets" to avoid putting in the work. I was running from the discomfort of challenging myself. But you know what? After a while something became ABUNDANTLY FREAKING CLEAR to me. Partial recovery land was actually a shit ton *less* comfortable than the eating disorder or full recovery was! I wasn't engaging fully in the eating disorder, so I lost the "safe" feeling of it, but I wasn't reaping the benefits of the freedom that full recovery brings either! That realization led to my decision to push myself.

So, what makes it so hard to get unstuck from partial recovery? Well, your eating disorder might be telling you in an effort to try to keep you trapped. We've outlined some of these below.

Lies Your Eating Disorder Tells Ya

1. *"Normal" people sometimes engage in disordered eating behaviors – so why can't I?*

Diet culture is super pervasive. Just because people without eating disorders may engage in some disordered eating behaviors, does NOT mean that you should. Even for people without eating disorders, engaging in behaviors such as skipping meals, calorie restriction, and rigid exercise is harmful and not healthy.

Additionally, part of struggling with an eating disorder is that you are not able to engage in disordered eating behaviors without keeping the eating disorder alive and running the risk that it will spread again like wildfire in times of stress.

It's sort of like someone with alcoholism saying, "well, normal people abuse alcohol sometimes so, why can't I?" This might feel unfair. However, it's actually the biggest gift that when you fully recover you won't have to have even a small percentage of your life shrouded by diet culture. You can eventually develop a better relationship with food, movement, and your body than people who've never struggled with an eating disorder. Kinda cool, right?

2. *Partial recovery is the best of both worlds.*

Your eating disorder might tell you that partial recovery is a good place to land and even label it as "the best of both worlds." It'll say that you can still maintain some sense of "control" and try to manage your weight – without being totally caught in your eating disorder. But contrary to what your eating disorder might tell you, partial recovery is actually *the worst* of both worlds.

In partial recovery, you might be doing somewhat better in your eating disorder, and people may appear less concerned. So, you might receive less support and understanding from others. However, you are still trapped by a voice in your head. Your eating disorder is not fully happy with you and neither is your authentic self. It's a lose-lose.

3. *I can choose to maintain at this level of disordered behavior.*

Your eating disorder may tell you that you can pick and choose "how sick" you stay and that you can maintain at this level of illness. However, this is utterly false. Staying in partial recovery is like saying "let's just leave 20 percent of this infection here." You might feel better for a time but it sits there waiting to spread at the next available opportunity.

Trying to maintain here is a recipe for a total relapse – especially during times of stress and life transitions. You simply CANNOT control whether your eating disorder will eventually get worse if you stay in partial recovery land.

4. *This is as good as it's gonna get – I can't fully recover.*

Most people who are fully recovered today never thought that they'd get there either. It's hard to envision a place that you have never been before. It's important to note that there can be real barriers in place that do make full recovery MUCH more difficult (i.e. access to treatment, weight stigma, financial barriers, or simply not having enough support).

However, we believe that continuing to strive for YOUR most fulfilled and strongest place in recovery is always worth it.

Ultimately, when you look back on your life in your 90's, wouldn't you rather be able to say that you gave it a full shot? You probably won't want to dwell in the regret that maybe you could have gotten to recovered if you hadn't given up, right? You can always go back to your eating disorder if you decide that recovered is not for you – but we don't know any recovered people who wish to do so.

5.   *I'm truly free from my eating disorder.*

Another lie that your eating disorder may tell you is that you are "recovered" even though you still have lingering thoughts and behaviors. We know that our eating disorders went through a few different iterations – from the more classic picture of anorexia to "wellness-informed" (read: eating disorder in disguise).

It can sometimes be hard to identify if you are still struggling because denial can run super deep. This is where it can be helpful to ask your treatment team, family, and friends, what they have noticed in terms of your behaviors and any concerns that they can identify. In order to treat a problem, you have to be willing to admit there is in fact a problem. Hence, coming to terms with the fact that you aren't fully or strongly recovered yet is an important step.

Tools for Getting Unstuck

1.   *Identify the lies that your eating disorder tells you around partial recovery and practice challenging them.*

So now we've practiced challenging the lies that your eating disorder is telling you around partial recovery. In order to really start to re-wire the neural pathways in your brain, it's SO important to put your coping statements into practice. You can put them into the "notes" section of your phone, set them as reminders in your phone, or record them and then play them back to yourself daily. Re-wiring your brain takes work – but so does an eating disorder – and only one pays off in the end.

2.   *Figure out the function of the remaining eating disorder behaviors and work to add in some healthier ways to get your needs met.*

Get mindful of the current eating disorder behaviors that you struggle with.
    Next to each behavior write down the function and then brainstorm some healthier ways to get your needs met.

Example:

Eating disorder behavior: Exercising X hours per week and feeling guilty if I miss any workouts.

Function: I feel safe, "in control," and it helps to calm my anxiety.

Alternate ways to meet needs: safe space visualization, soothing with my senses, think about pro-recovery behaviors that can help me to feel more empowered in my life (rather than false "control" from the eating disorder), meditation, talking to friends, meeting regularly with my therapist, taking my PRN anxiety medication.

3. *Identify your true values (vs. eating disorder values) and think about the ways in which staying in partial recovery interferes.*

For instance, let's say that you value relationships. However, your eating disorder values "thinness at all costs." It's likely that your rigid exercise routine negatively impacts your relationships on some level – so staying stuck in that behavior impacts one of your true values.

4. *Find recovered role models.*

It can be helpful for those stuck in quasi recovery to identify some recovered role models.

If you have people in your life who are recovered, you can ask them how they were able to get unstuck from partial recovery.

If you don't know anyone in "real life," find some inspirational stories, people online, or listen to podcasts that feature recovered people. You are definitely not alone in struggling with feeling stuck in partial recovery. However, getting to full recovery is 100% possible.

5. *Picture your life five years from now if you stay in partial recovery vs. five years from now if you were fully recovered.*

It can also be helpful to try to zoom out at the longer-term picture if you stay stuck in partial recovery. Imagine what your life could be like five years from now if you stay trapped in partial recovery vs. if you were fully recovered.

Table 11.1 Eating Disorder Values vs True Values

Eating Disorder Values	*True Values*

Partial Recovery: Five Years Out

Fully Recovered: Five Years Out

Jennifer

Oh partial recovery, AKA "the no man's land" of recovery. I remember when I thought that I was "doing so much better in recovery" when the reality was that I had just transfered my obsession onto something else. In one stage of my recovery, I became obsessed with "fitness." I wasn't restricting my food as much and in some ways my behaviors had improved, but I was still fixated on the appearance of my body and trying to change it. What I had uncovered was a more socially acceptable way to have an eating disorder. I had simply moved from a smaller cage into a bigger one. I was still trapped. I went through this stage of being stuck in a state of quasi recovery a few times in my journey (each at differing levels of denial) but I couldn't maintain there. When I tried to hold onto pieces of my eating disorder, my eating disorder just sat there waiting for the next life stressor to start to spread again like a wildfire.

You Deserve More

You deserve so much more than a life spent trapped in quasi recovery. While it's *so* tempting to tell yourself "this is as good as it's gonna get," trust us when we say that strong recovery or full recovery is a hell of a lot better.

Life is made to be lived FULLY in color – not stuck in black and white.

Journaling Prompts

1. List all of the remaining eating disorder behaviors and rules that you still struggle with.

2. Next to each eating disorder behavior list out the function.
   • Now brainstorm some healthier ways to get those needs met.
3. What are some of the things that are keeping you stuck in partial recovery?
4. What small steps could you add in to help move you forward?
5. If you look back on your life at age 90, will you regret staying stuck in partial recovery? If so, why?

12 All in the Fam
Where Do Our Loved Ones Come in?

We are going to paint a scene for you – you're chugging along, doin' the recovery thang, trying your hardest to just eat the damn donut, right? You actually go out to get a donut – because you are a badass who challenges the food police in your head regularly now. You sit down with your delectable-looking iced, sprinkled creation of joy. You breathe in, breathe out, and remind yourself of just what the hell you are fighting for – a life lived in color. Just as you go to take the first bite, your mom (or dad, or sister, or friend) walks into the room and exclaims "Wow that donut is HUGE."

Psssshhhhhhhhhhhh. That's the sound of the wind coming right out of your recovery sails. That's because comments like this have a tendency to get inside our heads and derail motivation during the recovery process. *Why* do family and friends always seem to say the wrong thing?? And *how* can you continue moving forward when these comments keep happening? Well, dear recovery buds, you are in luck. Because in this chapter, we will address why family and friends tend to always say the wrong thing. We will also give you strategies to help bring them on board with your recovery. Because the thing is – to beat this eating disorder, you are going to need support. You are going to need to rally the troops. Read on to learn how to do just that.

We hear about it during our sessions with clients at least once a day – a family member or friend said something triggering, and the comment highjacked our clients' entire day. Hell, we remember from our own recovery journeys – sometimes the people closest to us seem to know the *least* about how to help.

We believe that this is because eating disorders are not innately under-stood by those who do not struggle with them. It's hard to convey just how exhausting it is to have a voice in your head ordering you not to eat, or to eat far past fullness, day in and day out. Other mental illnesses are easier for onlookers to grasp. Take depression, for example. Most people who have not suffered from depression have at least experienced sadness in their lives. Same with anxiety – maybe those onlookers don't know what it is like to have clin-ical levels of depression or anxiety, but they can at least relate to the overall feeling. Eating disorders are a little different. Most everyone in our society has been impacted by diet culture. And most people have also experienced some internalized fatphobia because, let's face it, our society is fat-phobic as hell. But when the pressure to be thin, or the desire to restrict/eat past fullness, surpasses what is normative for people – that's when it gets tricky to relate to.

We've had parents who experience confusion, and say things like "how could my daughter be so high functioning at college? How can she achieve such great grades, and seem totally reasonable with every other aspect of her life, but cry inconsolably at the prospect of eating ice cream?"

We've had partners express utter bafflement. "Why would he make himself throw up? Why would anyone do that? Throwing up sucks."

You can't blame 'em really. Eating disorders do look a little illogical from the outside right? (Raise your hand if you have done some seriously weird shit to avoid eating that you would be embarrassed for others to know about (*raises hand sheepishly*).) Hence, the first step in gaining support is to help whoever in is your inner circle understand how it feels to be inside your head.

Side note – "inner circle" does not have to mean immediate family. Inner circle can be your chosen family. It can be your besties. It can be your partner. Hell, it can be your partner's besties. If your immediate family is not safe, whether that be emotionally, physically, or otherwise, then they would not be the appropriate support system for your recovery. It's up to YOU to decide who is safe and who might be helpful to bring on board.

Ok. Back to explaining stuff to your inner circle. Sometimes it helps to write out a small example of the dialogue that you have with the eating disorder inside your head. For example, take that donut dilemma that we started with. You could write out the initial eating disorder thoughts you had when going to purchase the donut, and how you challenged them:

EATING DISORDER: "Are you sureeee you want that? All those empty calories?"

SELF: "Yeah I want it. There is no such thing as empty calories."

EATING DISORDER: "What the actual f? Who told you that? Your treatment team? Gag. They're just trying to make you fat."

SELF: "1) Fat is not a dirty word. It's a neutral description of a body size. 2) They're trying to help me get my life back. 3) You're the one who is trying to kill me."

EATING DISORDER: "Listen, I'm just trying to help you make healthy choices ok? Donuts are objectively unhealthy. Eat! It's ok to eat! Just, like, only vegetables ok?"

SELF: "All foods fit. I don't need to limit myself to just vegetables."

EATING DISORDER: "You're weak if you eat that donut. You're disgusting and weak. You disappoint everyone around you."

SELF: "ARGGGGGGHHHH" *throws hands up in exasperation*

That's probably only a small snippet of what most people experience when they go to eat a fear food right? But even this snippet is *powerful* to see written out. For those who don't experience this mental battle, it can be helpful to see in this written format. It shows them what you might be too scared to say verbally. It gives them an inside glance into your struggle.

After writing something like this out, it can be helpful to sit down with your peeps and ask them if they have any questions. We highly recommend that you do this in a family therapy session. Why? Because a therapist has your back. If you get flustered or struggle to find your words, the therapist can jump in and help ya. You deserve that type of support when trying to explain such vulnerable stuff.

Jennifer

In my eating disorder, I didn't talk to many friends about what I was going through. I was worried about judgment and people not understanding or knowing what to say. This is definitely not an approach that I would recommend to others as I think that the more support that we can have the better. My family knew what I was struggling with and my mom participated in some of my dietitian sessions. What REALLY helped though, was when I agreed to let my mom take control of the meals for a little while. I was so scared of eating more, yet knew that I needed to. I remember being SO freaking scared of what she was serving, however in a way it helped to take the pressure off of me from having to make food choices.

Another way to help your inner circle help you? Provide them with a list of helpful things to say, and a list of unhelpful things to say. We know this sounds basic, but we have found that most family members and friends are grateful for this type of explicit instruction. Again, think back to the whole "this isn't innate" thing. It isn't innate for people who don't have an eating disorder to instantly understand that saying "you look healthy" can set off a grenade in your eating disorder mind. It isn't innate to know that saying "I understand" or cheering you on loudly can feel like shit. So let them know! What follows is a list of helpful and unhelpful statements that we (and our clients) have identified over the years:

What Not to Say:

- "You look so much healthier."
- "Wow, you've gained so much weight. You look great!"
- "You look so unhealthy/too thin/gross/sickly."
- "What have you eaten today?"
- "All you have to do is eat and exercise normally."
- "You look really different. Are you relapsing?"
- "You don't look like you have an eating disorder."
- "I wish I had your control and discipline."
- "That's really unhealthy and has a lot of calories."
- *Any talk of your own diet*
- "You have such a great life. How can you be struggling?"

What to Say:

- "I know it's difficult, and I'm so proud of you."
- "You're worth more than your eating disorder."
- "It's ok to take a rest day." (from exercise)
- "I'm here for you and I'm not going to leave."
- "I might not understand, but if you need someone to talk to, I'm here to listen and will help as much as I can."
- "How are you?"
- "I believe in you."
- "Let's do it together."
- "I love you/care about you."
- "I love your sense of humor, kindness, intellect, perseverance. etc." (something other than appearance)

Now, in the following spaces, try writing out a few of your own "what to say" statements and "what not to say" statements.

What to say:

....

....

....

What not to say:

....

....

....

Remember, your "what to say" and "what not to say" statements are allowed to evolve over time. It will be helpful to keep your inner circle in the loop about the evolution of what is helpful. These statements are super important because, remember, our loved ones are not mind readers. (We so much wish they were. Wouldn't life be a teeny bit easier if that was the case? We wish we were mind readers too because it would be pretty cool to be real-life therapy wizards.)

A Note on Getting Used to Asking for Support

It's ok if it feels weird to express yourself and your eating disorder thoughts to those around you. If you have had an eating disorder, you may have practice in using either your body or behaviors to express pain to those around you. Please don't feel ashamed of this. It is so common to fall into the trap of trying to obtain support or love in roundabout ways. If you have found yourself using your body as a canvas to express pain nonverbally, understand that you were surviving in the best way you knew how to at the time. That's it. You were not "attention seeking." You were not "manipulative." You were surviving. But now that you are taking the step towards recovery, it is time to find a new way to communicate. Because, let's face it, using our bodies and behaviors is not actually super effective in the end. We end up hurting ourselves in an attempt to gain support, versus obtaining the support in a healthy way.

Colleen

There were times when I felt my family had to be purposefully saying ALL THE WRONG THINGS. Spoiler alert: they weren't. They just didn't have eating disorders of their own, and so had no idea how a disordered voice can twist well-intentioned comments.

Example: I can recall how once, during a dark time when I was trying to dig myself out of a particularly nasty relapse, my dad earnestly looked at me and said "now you get to eat lots and lots of food. This could be kind of fun if you think about it!" I remember wanting to literally throw my coffee in his face. But looking back, this comment was honestly just an uninformed 50-year-old father's attempt to make his very ill daughter feel a little better.

After this comment, I remember supplying my parents with some reading material written by people with eating disorders of their own. While I myself wasn't brave enough to share just how this cruel voice in my head twisted their words, I was more than ok with allowing them to peer into someone else's disordered world. This could be an option for you as well if you, like me back then, are not ready to directly tell your parents what is personally triggering and what is helpful.

Once you've explained what it is like to experience an eating disorder, and provided your inner circle with the helpful and unhelpful statements, they are … likely still going to mess up. (Whomp whomp.) Hey, they're human! And remember – they will *not* get this right away. Try your hardest to internalize that, and foster some compassion for them (as long as it is obvious that they are trying). Practice correcting them when they say unhelpful things in a way that doesn't seem blamey or aggressive (i.e. "Telling me how huge the donut is makes my eating disorder very loud. Could you try telling me how delicious it looks?" or "Next time, it would be really helpful if you didn't comment on my food at all.")

Loved Ones Who are More Than Triggering

We want to make one thing very clear when it comes to friends and family – sometimes they are not able to support you in the way that you may need. While we have found that the majority of loved ones can be coached on how to be helpful, there is a small percentage of people who are just *stuck*. Stuck in diet culture, stuck in anger about your eating disorder, stuck in their own shit.

These are the parents who are committed to attending Weight Watchers meetings, even after having multiple discussions with you about Health at Every Size. These are the partners who can't seem to understand why meal-prepping their keto eats and then jetting off to crossfit can be difficult for you to deal with when you are trying to let go of obsessional exercise. These are the siblings who give you the silent treatment, because their anger about how your eating disorder has impacted their life leaves them unable to engage healthily with you.

Some of your loved ones may take years to educate. Some may never be able to change their diet culture-esque ways. In regard to these people, we suggest fostering compassion. Yes, it's so understandable if your first instinct is to feel angry with them. But try your damndest to look *underneath* that anger. What is the base feeling? (Aren't you glad we had that whole chapter devoted to understanding your feels?) We are guessing that it is most likely pain and sadness. Pain for yourself for feeling so unsupported and misunderstood in this battle. Sadness for them if they are caught up in diet culture. Consider acting in accordance with this base feeling, rather than with frustration or anger.

Journaling Prompt

Write an "unsendable letter" to your family members, telling them everything you wish they understood about your eating disorder. Say everything that you wish you could say. (Get mad! It's ok!)

Next, go through the letter and identify three "overarching themes." Overarching themes are basically major ideas and points that you want to get across. For example, it you wrote a lot about specific comments that they make about food, an overarching theme might be "I feel triggered when you speak about food in a negative manner." Other examples of overarching themes?

• I have used my body to communicate with you after feeling repeatedly shut down.
• I need you to tell me you love me more.
• I feel triggered by your own relationship with food and/or your body.

Look over those themes, and let them guide you towards understanding what is MOST important for you to be able to convey to your fam.

13 Body Image

Well, you knew it was coming, didn't you? It's time to talk about body image y'all. There are SO many myths and so much confusing information out there when it comes to eating disorders and body image. We're here to make things a little bit clearer for ya.

In this chapter, we are going to explain just what the hell body image even is. We're also going to talk about ways to *begin* the work of healing body image. We emphasize the word *begin* because this is a process that can take time (the same way that your negative body image likely didn't just develop overnight). So, try to be patient with yourself.

So, what is body image anyway?? The National Eating Disorders Association (NEDA) defines body image as "how you see yourself when you look in the mirror or when you picture yourself in your mind" (NEDA, n.d.). Body image includes how we feel and think about our appearance – including our height, shape, weight, hair, facial features, etc. It also includes how we feel about our body functioning, and how we physically experience being in our bodies.

As you can tell, body image is far more complicated than just seeing yourself as "fat" or "thin." It encompasses a huge range of thoughts and emotions that we have about these sacks of flesh that we all reside in. That's the thing about body image – it is *hugely* important, because it is essentially how we feel about the home that we live in, from birth until the day we die. It's probably no surprise, then, that feeling badly about our bodies can impact nearly every facet of life.

Research shows that negative body image is correlated with low self-esteem, which can then in turn impact our social lives, romantic relationships, school performance, careers, family lives – basically every facet of life that could be impacted WILL be impacted by negative body image (van den Berg et al., 2010). This is important stuff. Body image concerns are not "fluff." Struggling with your body image does not make you "vain." Your struggle is so valid, and so worth healing – do you hear us?? Good. Because one thing that we hear time and time again from our clients is this idea that they should just be able to "get over" negative body image – that something about this struggle is inherently silly or self-absorbed. Do you sometimes feel this way? Well then hand us the megaphone, because we are here to shout from the rooftops that YOUR BODY IMAGE STRUGGLE IS VALID, AND YOUR BODY IMAGE IS WORTH FOCUSING ON!

Whew. Now that that's out of the way, we can move on to more important shit. Because we know what you are thinking: "Ok Colleen and Jennifer – loud and clear. I feel badly about my body and it's a worthy feeling. Cool cool. Soooo what am I supposed to do with that?"

Well, before you can heal your body image, you sort of have to understand what came together to create such intense feelings of loathing towards your flesh suit. We always like to say that our bodies are simply our vessels that we use to move around and get through life. Over time, we begin to attach meaning and emotions to these vessels, and create stories in our minds about them. These stories have less to do with our actual bods, and way more to do with our life experiences that feed into what we come to believe about our bods. Think about it – is an infant born feeling self-conscious about their body image? Do they come out of the womb saying, "just a little breastmilk for me Mamadukes – I'm trying to slim down these thighs"? Laughable right? Babies have no concept that they are supposed to hate their bodies (yet). That concept is handed to them by their family members, friends, society, the media, and our general cultural messaging.

While there are several usual suspects when it comes to origins of negative body image, your unique narrative about your body is going to stem from different places than our unique narratives. That's why it is important to figure out for yourself, "just what the hell happened to make me hate my body so much?" Here are some common suspects:

Diet Culture

We live in diet culture. It is the sea that we are all swimming in. You can't swing an intuitive eating book without hitting a hundred "keto guide to weight loss" books. Our society is *obsessed* with losing weight. We all seem to be obsessed with the thin body ideal. The message that we are given from day 0 is clear: "there is only one type of acceptable body (very thin), and you should do everything in your power to try to achieve this body type while you are living on this earth." Other diet culture-esque societal messages include, "if you are living in a larger body, you are doomed" and "you should always put losing weight and the way you look above everything else in life."

It is only natural that we absorb these messages as we grow up. In fact, they seem to infiltrate our psyche before we have any realization. Research shows that around 24% of children as young as 3 years old demonstrate negative body image, and report a desire to diet. The number jumps to 47% by age 6 (PACEY, 2016). It makes sense, right? Weight loss ads are on billboards, on tv, on the magazines that we leave laying around for our kids to pick up. Of course, young children are going to start noticing something is up. And furthermore – check out any kids flicks recently? What type of bodies do the princesses always seem to have? Ultra thin bods, right? And the princes are all slender and buff. But the villains? Well they are almost universally fat. It's ridiculous how much this tends to hold up if you start to take a look at the movies meant for kids. So of course, children internalize this. After all, who wants to look like the fat, mean, evil villain when you can look like the petite, beautiful princess who is dressed by birds and lands the prince?

So, it's pretty understandable that diet culture messaging eventually seeps in and comes to impact the way that we feel about our bodies.

Modeling From Others

Another huge factor when it comes to shaping body image? Modeling from others. As we grow up, we receive messages from those around us that provide information about how we should feel about our bodies. This modeling can come from a variety of people in our lives. Our parents, our siblings, our aunts, our uncles, our teachers, our coaches, our peers – anyone that we look up to or care about can influence the stories that we learn to tell ourselves about our bods. For example, take your mom. Your good ol' ma. Chances are, she was one of the first people who influenced how you feel towards your body. Why? Because our parents are our first teachers. It is tough to grow up caring for and respecting your body if your first teacher is constantly berating her own body. When our parents talk about their bodies in negative ways, we, as kids, internalize the seed "They don't like their bodies. I am supposed to not like mine." This seed can then be watered by messages from other people in our lives, diet culture, and the media.

Other family members can also plant these negative body image seeds. Maybe you have an older sister who constantly referred to herself as "chubby" in a negative manner. Maybe your brother used to talk about needing to "eat clean" to lower his body fat ratio. These messages don't just bounce off of us. They seep in.

Coaches, teachers, tutors, peers – anyone who talks negatively about their own body around us can contribute to the developing of our body image. We can recall specific people in *our* lives – a babysitter who talked about dieting – a friend's mother who called herself "porky" – these people slowly but surely provided sentences that we each added to our own personal body image narratives. We are not blaming these people for our negative body image or eating disorders, nor are we encouraging you to completely blame the people in your lives. But make no mistake about it – modeling from others is *hugely* important when it comes to body image.

Upbringing

Another factor that impacts the stories we tell ourselves about our bods, which is related to modeling but not exactly the same, is our upbringing. You see, we all grow up in these unique little societies – these societies are our families. Each family comes with its own history and its own attitudes towards bodies and food. These attitudes influence the development of our own attitudes. Let us explain:

Say your grandparents grew up during the great depression. Food scarcity was a thing, and it ended up impacting the way that they thought about food for the rest of their lives. Your parents, then, would have grown up in a household in which the attitude around food was, perhaps, *strict* and *serious*. Perhaps they were told to always clean their plates. Perhaps they were given the message that food is for fuel, and that our individual likes and dislikes matter very little. Maybe your grandparents were also thin by nature and thus your parents internalized the message that thin was good, and that thinness = strength/toughness. Your parents would then likely develop a scarcity mindset around food, and an idealization of thin bodies. Then you come along – born into a family society that fuels a scarcity mindset in terms of eating, and the idea that it is important to have a thin body. You then internalize these messages, and they come to impact the story that you tell yourself about your own body.

See what we mean? Each generation builds a unique message that becomes our family narrative. This message, then, in turn, greatly shapes our own thoughts and feelings about both food and our bods.

Colleen

I have seen this intergenerational messaging about food and weight passed down in a very blatant way. As I mentioned in the introduction, my grandmother struggled with an eating disorder for the entirety of her adult life. The struggle did not end when she had my father. He recalls her talking incessantly about her weight throughout his childhood. He also tells stories of how she attempted to "curb her kids' appetites" by feeding them smaller amounts than they generally asked for. In turn, my father internalized the message that fat is bad, and that thin is something that adults must always strive for. He has also always struggled with a sort of rigid attitude towards things like time of the day when he is "allowed" to eat. He accidentally handed this message about food rigidity to me through his own behaviors, and also handed me some of his fatphobia via negative comments about fat bodies. To be clear – none of this was intentional! Poor guy had no idea what he was doing. Just like his mother honestly probably did not know either. But I do. The buck stops here. By tracing this back, I am able to understand where some of these body image stories in my head have come from. I can then decide if I want to keep these stories (spoiler alert: I don't!) and then make the change to stop this intergenerational transfer of pain. My children will not be the recipients of these subconscious messages about food and body. Mark my words.

Media Messaging

Ah yes, the media. Another source of information that contributes to our body image narratives. The media provides us with information about how we "should" be feeling about our bodies. It provides us with constant imagery of the thin ideal. It provides us with messaging that insinuates that being fat is bad. Basically, the media is a monster that constantly feeds our negative body images in both blatant and insidious ways.

Think we are being dramatic when we use the term "monster" to describe the media? Think again friends. Digital marketing experts suggest that we are exposed to around 4,000 media images *every damn day* (Marshall, 2015). That is more than our grandparents were exposed to in a year. Can you even begin to fathom how absolutely wild that is? The amount of imagery that we are exposed to is excessive. We see so many images that we don't even realize they *are* images! From commercials, to magazines, to internet ads, to highway signs, to movies, to television shows – we are being bombarded with images of the thin ideal from every direction – and it takes its toll.

Do not downplay the significance of how this imagery impacts our psyche. One study demonstrated the impact that media can have on body image quite vividly: researchers polled females in a remote area – a province of Fiji's main island, Viti Levu – on their body image and disordered eating behavior. They then introduced television to the island. After only three years, the rates of negative body image and disordered eating jumped *significantly.* Twenty-nine percent of the females polled scored highly when tested for their eating-disorder risk, as compared to 13% just three years prior (Goode, 1999). It is pretty clear that the images around us contribute to how we end up feeling towards our bodies.

The current body ideal that is promoted in our culture is thin. Yes, there are some people who say that we have made progress from the "heroine chic" thin ideal of the 90s (think *Ally McBeal, Sex and the City*, Kate Moss, etc.). These people will say that celebs have more diversity when it comes to their bodies – they will cite "curvy" women such as Kim Kardashian as evidence for how far we have come.

Bullshit. Kim Kardashian is yet another body type that is unattainable for 99.9% of us. She may be "curvy," but make no mistake – her body is a very specific ideal (large hips, small waist, large breasts). Similar to ultra thin "heroin chic" – Kim Kardashian's body is a body type that most of us will not be able to achieve. It's biologically impossible for most of us. Plus, her body is still thin, so the thin ideal is also being promoted.

All of these ideal images, these celebrity bodies, this culture of constant imagery via social media – it seeps in and impacts our body image narratives. There is just no way around it.

Trauma

This one is so important that we have a whole chapter on it. But we still felt like it was worth mentioning here. Trauma can very much impact the way we end up feeling in our bodies. As we talked about before, trauma, and especially sexual trauma, happens *to* our bodies. So, it is understandable that a direct result can be an alteration of how we feel in our bodies afterwards.

Sexual trauma essentially teaches our brain that we are not safe in our bodies. This feeling of not being safe can then manifest in different ways for different people. For example, some people begin to feel disgusted towards their body. Some people begin to feel angry towards their body. Some people internalize blame, and begin to focus on controlling their bodies in an attempt to ward off future sexual trauma. The takeaway point is, trauma happens *to* our bodies. So, it is no wonder that it impacts how we feels *towards* our bodies.

Oppression

We simply cannot talk about the development of negative body image without also talking about the role of oppression and marginalization. Black people, indigenous people, and people of color (BIPOC) face racial-based oppression day in and day out. The hard truth is, it is more dangerous to exist in a Black or brown body. This lack of safety impacts body image. How could it not? Feelings of being unsafe in your body will inevitably lead to feelings of wanting to reject your body. Additionally, our gross Eurocentric standards of beauty create unfair "standards" for BIPOC people to strive for. The combination of being given the message that your skin, hair, or features are wrong, coupled with the systemic racism that is threaded throughout our society, is a tinderbox for eating disorders and horrible body image.

Transgender individuals also face body-based oppression, which has been shown to create negative body image. The experience of gender dysphoria is, in and of itself, a huge strain on body image. Tack on discrimination and oppression from every angle in our society, and it is not hard to see how body image (and one's overall relationship with one's body) suffers.

Eating Disorders

Ok so this one is sort of a chicken or the egg scenario. Does negative body image cause an eating disorder, or does an eating disorder cause negative body image? Our answer is...both! We know that negative feelings towards our bodies are one of the main risk factors for the development of eating disorders. (Dieting is the other huge risk factor.) But the thing is, once you begin to engage in a cycle of disordered eating, your relationship with your body begins to be impacted. For example, we noticed for ourselves that our body image became more fragile when we lost weight in our eating disorders. This is similar to what a lot of our clients report too. In fact, the majority of our clients say that they have never been more obsessed with weight, or felt crappier about their bodies than when they were actively eating disordered. This is because, much of the time, weight loss does not actually improve body image. It's hard to feel good about your body when you are starving it. Furthermore, if your eating disorder does not result in weight loss (because the vast majority do not), your body image might be negatively impacted by the frustration and anger you feel about this. Put it this way – treating our bodies like absolute shit does not, in fact, make us love them more. We might experience fleeting feelings of self-confidence that stem from weight loss, but this self-confidence tends to be unstable and surface-level.

Weight Stigma

Weight stigma impacts body image, so very much. We saved this one for last because it is such an important piece of the body image puzzle. We live in a weight-obsessed society. This does not just mean that we are obsessed with losing weight. This also means that those who are in larger bodies are marginalized. Basically, our society treats fat people terribly. Fat bodies are demonized by the media, the medical profession, the job industry, and more. Our society is not set up to accommodate larger bodies. Think about it. What is the message that we are sending when we do not have plane seats, restaurant booths, or even life-saving medical equipment that fit all bodies? The message is that your body is wrong. It is wrong, and it is on fat folks to fix their bodies. Instead of fitting our society around people's bodies, we ask people to fit their bodies around societal standards. This is RIDICULOUS and so unfair. So obviously, weight stigma plays a role in our body image. And it is safe to say that those in larger bodies will have a harder time healing negative body image than those in smaller bodies. Yes, this is a tough truth. But you didn't pick up our book for a sugar-coated perspective on recovery, did you? We want to be very clear here – we refuse to ignore the impact that weight stigma has on recovery. We refuse to gloss over the fact that being in a larger body creates an added layer of intense difficulty in our society.

So now that you are a verified expert on the underlying factors that play into our body image, take a moment to complete your very own "body image iceberg" (see Figure 13.1) This is an exercise that we often use with our clients to help them unearth all those teeny and not-so-teeny variables that have played into how they presently feel about their bodies:

Simply fill out the bottom of the iceberg with all of the societal, cultural, and personal variables that you believe led you to where you are today in terms of your relationship with your body.

Figure 13.1 Body Image Iceberg

So...What Can You Do About It?

We're glad you asked! First, you've taken an amazing first step by writing down your own body image iceberg. We always say that insight is the flashlight. With that iceberg, you are shining a flashlight into the recesses of your soul – the dark parts that have festered, fed by a sick society, ridiculous-feckin' cultural standards, family history, personality attributes, and more. But now that you have identified what is making you feel like shit about your body, the next step is to...you guessed it! Change.

We recommend taking the following steps to kick start your journey to healing your body image:

1. *Write down some of the recent stories that your mind has been telling you about your body.*
    - Next to each story, write the emotions that come up, and any urges.
    - Rather than asking if the story is true, ask yourself, is it helpful in terms of getting you in the direction of a meaningful life?
2. *Begin to notice and take inventory of just when and where you experience the strongest negative body image thoughts.*
    - Ask yourself, is there anything else that is bothering me or causing me stress? Yes? Might I then be numbing out this experience or emotion by shifting focus onto my body?

- Remember – negative body image is like a pair of comfortable, ratty yoga pants that you put on after a long day. The yoga pants are your go-to. They provide a natural sense of ease and familiarity. But the thing is, there are other, more comfortable pieces of loungewear, wayyyy in the back of your closet that you have forgotten about. These pieces are less ratty. Less beat up. In fact, you might actually find they are softer and more pleasing to have on after all those years of the ratty yoga pants! Do you get where we are going with this? Are you picking up what we're laying down? *Those less worn out pieces of loungewear are the new coping skills that you can learn to use after a long, hard day.* Instead of funneling all negative emotions and thoughts into "I hate my body," or "I feel disgusting," you can try journaling about the actual emotion you are experiencing. A good journaling prompt for this would be:
- *I feel ugly and gross, but feelings are not facts. What I am really feeling is….*
- By completing that one journaling assignment, you have just taken a step towards changing out of those old ratty yoga pants. (Who needs 'em right?)

3. Another really important step to healing your body image is to start doggedly asking yourself, "what do I believe that my ideal body will bring me?" Truly. What does your mind trick you into believing about that thigh gap or flat tummy? Do you believe this will bring you confidence? Lasting happiness? A partner? More friends? More peace in life overall? This is important to piece apart because once you do, you will likely begin to see that your ideal body will probably not, in fact, bring you these things. It may bring you a faux sort of confidence, sure. We get that. But confidence at what cost? What does this confidence and fleeting sense of safety mean if you have to commit to micromanaging your time and life around maintaining a weight that your bod will fight back against? Here is (yet another… are you sensing a theme yet with this book?) journaling prompt to jumpstart your thoughts and insights about this:

   In pursuing my ideal body, I am really pursuing…. What are some other, healthier ways that I can meet this need?

4. Yet another, really important question to ask yourself is: "How is body bashing serving me?" What needs are you trying to meet by being mean to your body? For us, some of these needs were perfectionism and the ability to feel lovable or worthy. We shit-talked and bullied our bodies in a misguided effort to achieve the golden fountain of worth and happiness. We did so by pursuing "perfection" for our bodies. Hot take – there is no such thing. Turns out, we could meet the needs for worthiness and loveability in a variety of other, more sustainable ways. One such way was reminding ourselves of our inherent worth. Try repeating this mantra to yourself: *I am worthy just by being born.* Our

culture tells us that we need to prove ourselves worthy and enough – but the truth is, that's BS! We are all worthy of love, attention, and happiness just by the mere fact that we exist. (So, capitalism and the glorification of busy can go screw itself, yeah? Yeah.)

5.   Another really simple way to combat your negative body image is to surround yourself with images of body diversity. Research has demonstrated time and time again that humans tend to find a person more attractive the more they see that person. In other words, familiarity breeds attraction. In psychology land, this is referred to as the "mere exposure effect" (Berscheid & Ammazzalorso, 2001). Hence it makes sense that an important step towards finding beauty among diverse body types is to surround yourself and constantly be exposing yourself to diverse body types! One easy way to do this is through social media. Following accounts of those in diverse body types is a way to help you re-wire your neural pathways so that you eventually begin to accept these body types as normal, neutral, or even beautiful. (Side note – we don't just mean following accounts of those in larger bodies. We suggest you follow accounts of people across marginalizations – i.e. trans and non-binary folks, folks of different races and ethnicities and folks of varying disabilities.)

An important point about all this body image jazz is to have some effing self-compassion! This stuff is really, really, really hard. It is no easy task to unlearn society's messages to hate yourself. The re-wiring of those neural pathways (i.e. finding the newer loungewear to put on) takes a ton of time, and dogged effort. But you can. You can. You can.

Jennifer

Body image was a BIG struggle for me especially after weight restoring in my recovery. I remember feeling disgusted with the image looking back at me, while the eating disorder voice yelled at me that I needed to restrict my food and that "I'd let myself go." One of my first therapists tried to help remind me that the appearance of my body wasn't all that important – and that we were all going to change as we age. This sentiment helped, but it wasn't until I found the Health At Every Size® movement that things truly started to shift for me. At first, I was just tolerating my body. Truly, I hated the appearance of my body and could hardly even look at it. Over time, and through therapy, I was able to eventually get to a place of feeling slightly less negative about my body – then to feeling neutral – and now to have moments where I appreciate my body, but more importantly am generally not focused on its appearance because I'm too busy living my best life!

Table 13.1 Negative Body Image Self-Talk

Negative body image thought/ overheard negative body image chatter:	Negative body image thought/ overheard negative body image chatter:	Negative body image thought/ overheard negative body image chatter:	Negative body image thought/ overheard negative body image chatter:	Negative body image thought/ overheard negative body image chatter:	Negative body image thought/ overheard negative body image chatter:	Negative body image thought/ overheard negative body image chatter:	Negative body image thought/ overheard negative body image chatter:	Negative body image thought/ overheard negative body image chatter:
What I would say now:	What I would say now:	What I would say now:	What I would say now:	What I would say now:	What I would say now:	What I would say now:	What I would say now:	What I would say now:

Journaling Prompts

1. Write down ten instances in which you have engaged in negative body image self-talk, or heard somebody else engaging in negative body image self-talk and not said anything. Then, next to each instance, write "what I would say now is…" Know better, do better.
2. Decades from now, what would you want your gravestone to say? You heard us right. In the following space, write down what you would want written on your gravestone.

We are betting that you didn't write "Here lies____. She was able to fit into very small jeans her whole life." Or "Here lies _____ His arms stayed toned well into old age." Why is this important? Because what you want on your gravestone is likely a reflection of what you want to be remembered for. Next time negative body image is consuming your thoughts, remind yourself of your authentic, gravestone self – and try to shift your attention to that.

References

Berscheid, E. & Ammazzalorso, H. (2001). Emotional experience in close relationships. In G.J.O. Fletcher & M.S. Clark (Eds.), *Blackwell Handbook of Social Psychology* (Vol. 2, pp. 308–330). Oxford, UK: Blackwell.

Goode, E. (1999, May 20). Study finds TV alters Fiji girls' view of body. The New York Times. www.nytimes.com/1999/05/20/world/study-finds-tv-alters-fiji-girls-view-of-body.html

Marshall, R. (2015). How many ads do you see in one day? Red Crow Marketing. www.redcrowmarketing.com/2015/09/10/many-ads-see-one-day/

NEDA (n.d.) Body image. www.nationaleatingdisorders.org/body-image-0

PACEY (2016). Children as young as 3 unhappy with their bodies. Professional Association for Childcare and Early Years. www.pacey.org.uk/news-and-views/news/archive/2016-news/august-2016/children-as-young-as-3-unhappy-with-their-bodies/

van den Berg, P., Mond, J., Eienburg, M., Ackard, D., & Neumark-Sztainer, D. (2010). The link between body dissatisfaction and self-esteem in adolescents: similarities across gender, age, weight status, race/ethnicity, and socioeconomic status. *Journal of Adolescent Health*, 47(3): 290–296.

14 Gym-Timidation
How to Move for Joy

The sun is starting to rise filling the sky with pink and orange hues. You're running. Sweat drips down your back as your feet pound down on the pavement. Your legs are burning, yet you feel like you can't stop. You log the miles in your phone. You're only "allowed" to stop when you hit a certain number – even though it's starting to feel like your legs are about to freaking give out. Your friends praise "your dedication" in waking up at sunrise to run so many miles before your day starts. What they don't know is that it's not "dedication" that keeps you running every morning – you are trapped in an eating disorder and exercise compulsion.

Sounds familiar? We hear ya friends. Exercise and eating disorders. Let's go:

Ok, so here's the deal: when it comes to recovery, exercise can be a really tricky topic (understatement of the year). Fitness culture doesn't help with this at all. Instead, it promotes and normalizes a disordered relationship with exercise. Sorry fitspo, but you're not healthy and we're *so* over you.

So how do you know if you are struggling with an unhealthy relationship to exercise?

Red Flags of an Unhealthy Relationship with Exercise:

- Rigid, inflexible exercise routine.
- Guilt/anxiety if exercise routine is disrupted.
- Exercising despite illness, injury, weather, or just simply "not feeling like it."
- Missing social functions in order to exercise.
- Withdrawing from friends and family.
- Tying exercise to eating (i.e. telling yourself "if I don't exercise, then I have to eat less.")
- Fearing that you might gain weight if you take time off from exercise

Identify Your Red Flags

_____

_____

_____

_____

_____

_____

_____

Another question to ask yourself is: what percentage of your day (0–100%) do you spend thinking about exercise?

_____

If your exercise routine is disrupted, what percentage of your day (0–100%) do you spend thinking about exercise?

_____

Compulsive exercise is a socially acceptable prison cell. We know – we've both been there and we were able to find a way out. We struggled with symptoms including, engaging in punishing workouts, frantically trying to run away from our problems at the gym, equating food with exercise and feeling unable to stop.

Jennifer

Compulsive exercise was a major struggle for me. I felt like I had to do X amount of time at the gym every day in order to feel "ok." I also felt unable to take a day off from exercise. Even when I had strep throat, I still worked out. It was torture. Part of me really wanted to be free from compulsive exercise but the other part was terrified. I also tied exercise with food and when I eventually was able to take a rest day (shoutout to therapy!) I struggled with feeling like I "didn't deserve to eat." I remember taking that first rest day from exercise like it was yesterday. I felt like I was crawling out of my skin and couldn't think about anything else. I was miserable. But the more that I gradually challenged my exercise rules, the easier that it got over time. I learned how to nourish my body even when I wasn't moving at all, to enjoy days where I didn't move my body, and to find forms of joyful movement (i.e. walking outside on a nice day or having a solo dance party). This, for me, was probably one of the hardest aspects of my eating disorder to overcome, however it's so incredibly rewarding to no longer be tied to a rigid exercise routine.

Ok So You Know It's a Problem – What Next?

We've got some tips for recovering from compulsive exercise and we can't wait to share 'em with you:

1.   Start by being mindful.

The first step towards changing ANY behavior is starting by cultivating mindfulness of it. Mindfulness is being aware in the present moment (without judgment) and observing our thoughts and feelings without getting caught up in them (Headspace, n.d.). Essentially, it's learning how to explore and be present with what is currently happening.

The way that we like to describe mindfulness is through this example:

Being caught up in your thoughts and emotions is like being in the middle of a storm, in the rain, without an umbrella.

Mindfulness is when you are able to see the storm going on from behind a window. The storm is still happening but you can observe it and not get entangled in it. We want to turn this mindful awareness to your current thoughts, feelings, and behaviors surrounding exercise.

We'll start with a word association exercise. Underneath the word "exercise" we want you to write any words/thoughts/feelings that come to mind.

Exercise

Now, observe your answers – trying not to judge them.

Next, underneath the word "rest" we want you to write any words/thoughts/feelings that come to mind.

Rest

We'll come back to this later, but for now just take a moment to observe your answers.

Throughout your week, try to be mindful of any thoughts and feelings that are associated with exercise. It's also helpful to observe your specific behaviors and check for signs of rigidity, guilt, and compulsiveness around exercise.

Just like we talked about in the chapter on body image, it can also be helpful to think about where the heck your beliefs and ideas around exercise came from. As a very little kid, you likely weren't thinking about "moving for weight loss," so when did exercise become tied to trying to change your body for you?

2. Work to challenge any exercise rules.

The next step is to start to challenge those exercise rules, which are keeping you trapped in this compulsive exercise prison.

On a separate piece of paper, list out all of your current exercise rules. *Examples:*

- I have to exercise X number of times a week.
- I have to do X workout in order for it "to count."
- I can't eat as much if I haven't exercised.

There are two different approaches to challenging exercise rules. Both are recommended and it's up to you (and your treatment team if you have one) to decide what will work best for you.

Cold Turkey

Taking some time completely off from exercise can be that re-boot that you need. We highly recommend considering taking some time off from exercise in order to begin to recreate your relationship to movement. We know this can feel SO freaking difficult at first – however, over time it will get easier to give your body weeks (or months) to rest and recharge.

Gradual Approach

Another approach is to do things more gradually (challenging those pesky exercise rules!), i.e. starting by shaving off ten minutes a day from your exercise routine. (Hey! Colleen here! This is an approach that was helpful for me when I was struggling with compulsively running. I started out running a little less each week, and eventually – with a lot of time and therapy – fell into a groove that no longer felt punishing – spoiler alert: the amount that felt joyful for me to run was far less than what I had been making myself do.)

The Aim

The goal here is to break every one of your exercise rules, so that you can eventually rebuild a healthier and more joyful relationship with movement.

Pro-Tip

If you are trying to break exercise rules, think about the variables that are keeping you stuck and work to eliminate them.

Ideas

- Throw out your Fitbit or activity tracker (we'll be over here cheering you on with this one. We know it can be so tough!)
- Donate or throw away your running shoes.
- Cancel that gym membership.

What I can cut out that's keeping me stuck:

_____

_____

_____

_____

3. *Add in more values-aligning coping strategies.*

Compulsive exercise is currently serving a function in your life – or you wouldn't be engaging in it. It's important to start to look at the purpose that compulsive exercise is serving in your life, so that we can try to get your needs met in more values-aligning ways.

If your compulsive exercise had a "job," what would it be?

Examples: My compulsive exercise helps to numb me out from my life, cope with my past trauma, and deal with low self-worth.

Job Description (Compulsive Exercise):

**write out YOUR job description for compulsive exercise.

_____

_____

_____

_____

_____

Values-Aligning Ways of Getting Needs Met

*Now that you've gotten more familiar with the functions of compulsive exercise in your life, try to think of more values-aligning ways to get some of those needs met.

Example:

Need: anxiety management
Values-Aligning Coping Strategies: meditation, playing with a pet, squeezing putty, reviewing mantras, reaching out for support, safe space visualization.

Need:
Values-Aligning Coping Strategies:

Need:
Values-Aligning Coping Strategies:

Need:
Values-Aligning Coping Strategies:

Need:
Values-Aligning Coping Strategies:

4. *Practice Coping with Distress*

When you start to challenge your rules around exercise, you will experience a TEMPORARY increase in distress. This can cause people to want to throw in the towel, but it truly is a sign of progress (for real!). It's important to practice letting yourself feel uncomfortable. Part of recovery is all about gettin' comfortable with feeling discomfort.

Radical Acceptance

One helpful skill for coping with distress comes from dialectical behavior therapy (DBT). It's called "radical acceptance" (Gill, 2013). Radical acceptance means accepting reality as is. It doesn't mean that you like or agree with something – rather it acknowledges that suffering comes from pain + non-acceptance (Gill, 2013). So, in order to ease suffering, acceptance is necessary. It can be useful to accept the fact that challenging your exercise rules may feel distressing as hell in the beginning and that's ok and normal. However, over time you will learn that the distress will naturally come down on its own – so long as you can sit with it.

Debunking an Exercise Myth

This one may surprise you, but did you know that long-term studies show that being on exercise programs doesn't cause people to lose a significant amount of weight (Bacon, 2010)? Exercise is simply NOT the weight loss panacea that the media hypes it to be.

For instance,

> The Women's Health Study evaluated almost 40,000 women and determined that the difference in body mass index between those with the highest level of exercise and the lowest was only about .4. The Harvard Alumni Study compared more than 12,000 men who regularly participated in various intensities of exercise and similarly, found a difference of less than five pounds. These results are consistent with many other studies.
>
> (Bacon, 2010, p. 140)

There are numerous factors that play into this, but the most important take away is that exercise has NOT been shown to have a dramatic impact on weight – despite what the media messages and your eating disorder might tell you (Bacon, 2010), which is totally fine, in our opinion. There are many other benefits to exercise that have nothing to do with weight. Let's focus on those! Now you can start to explore other motivations (what up joy?) for movement that have nothing to do with attempting to change your body.

Sometimes Rest is the Healthiest Choice

If you are tired, ill, injured, or simply don't feel like it, rest may be the HEALTHIEST choice for you in that moment. Despite what diet culture might say, "more exercise" is not always better and it's crucial to give your body time to rest and recharge, especially as exercise is a stressor on the body.

The American Council on Exercise states that:

> exercise creates two types of stress on your muscles: metabolic stress that comes from depleting the energy stored in individual muscle cells and mechanical stress created by physical damage to the structures of muscle proteins. While the body experiences metabolic or mechanical stress during exercise, it's during the recovery period after the exercise that the body repairs the muscle proteins and replaces the glycogen (stored glucose in liver and muscle tissue) used to fuel the workout.
>
> (McCall, 2018)

It's also important to point out that there is NO moral obligation to engage in any kind of formal "exercise routine" at all. None whatsoever. Seriously. Ragen Chastain, a totally rad fat activist, sums it up best when she says,

> let's be clear: nobody is obligated to participate in fitness of any kind, not everyone has the same access to movement options, and participation in movement is not a barometer of worthiness...I can tell you

for sure that running a marathon and having a Netflix marathon are morally equivalent activities.

(Chastain, n.d.)

Our culture places such an emphasis on "productivity," busyness, and exercise, that ultimately we forget the importance of rest and relaxation.

Moving for Joy

So, how can you tell if someone has a positive relationship to movement?

The following are a few signs that someone has a positive relationship to movement:

- Movement is flexible, varied, and free from any "rules."
- Movement is enjoyable – rather than coming from attempts at "control" or self-punishment.
- Taking time off from movement invokes no feelings of guilt or distress.
- Able to eat freely regardless of if movement has occurred.

It all comes down to intention and motivation.

For instance, two people might decide to go for a walk. One person thinks about how beautiful the weather is and decides to walk around the block to enjoy the sunshine and feeling of the wind blowing through their hair. They are able to turn around when they start feeling tired. The other person just ate a large meal and is feeling guilty about what they have eaten. They go for the walk with a focus on "burning calories" and have a set amount of time that they feel like they "should" walk for. Same action – but one intention is coming from a place of fear, whereas the other is coming from a place of joy.

We want to note that it can be hard to tease out true intentions (vs. eating disorder intentions) when you are deeply struggling with an eating disorder – which is why a break from exercise all together is so recommended.

Colleen

Y'all – if I had to pick a "hardest part" of my recovery process, this would be it. Movement. If you could have seen how many knock-down-drag-out arguments that I had with therapists back in the day about how "my exercise is NOT disordered OK? IT'S FUN FOR ME"…well you might get a little judgey. (Actually, what am I saying? I'm sure you wouldn't judge. You're reading this book after all. You are my people.)

I think this was hard for me because movement was there for me before my eating disorder. In high school I ran track for fun. I wasn't any star athlete. I wasn't the best. And I was fine with that! It was just for fun – at first. It was my eating disorder that turned running into a chore – a personal whipping regime meant to compensate for any food I had eaten each day. It got to a point where I was putting myself in actual danger – a low point was when I snuck out of my house during a hurricane to run. My eating disorder used the fact that running had started out as something positive against me. It literally tricked me into thinking that I couldn't give up running – that I didn't have to in order to recover. "Running isn't part of this," I told countless therapists.

In the end, it took getting really freaking honest with myself about my motivates for running. It also took gradual reduction in exercise time and intensity, and some formal breaks altogether. These reductions and breaks were CRUCIAL steps to help me heal my relationship with running specifically. I guess I want to share this with you all because I want you to know that it is ok if this is a crucial step for you as well. Specifically, extended breaks from formal exercise (we're talking 6+ months here) can be an uncomfortable but truly amazing step in freeing yourself from the binds of compensatory behavior.

So, you've challenged your exercise rules, taken some time off from movement, and are looking to rebuild a more joyful relationship with it – wondering where to start? We've got your back.

1.   Think back to childhood.

If you had a positive relationship with movement as a kid, try to think about the activities that you enjoyed doing back then. Did you like playing outside, walking around the block, kicking around a soccer ball, or hula hooping?

As we get older, often we lose that same sense of wonder and joy that we felt as children.

Thinking back to what you enjoyed as a kid might give you some insights into the type of movement that you might find joyful now.

What kind of movement (if any) did you do as a kid:

_____
_____
_____
_____

2.   Try out something new.

Rather than defaulting to the type of movement that you did in your eating disorder, think about exploring some new forms of movement.

Ideas:

- A yoga class
- Dancing to music in your room
- Playing pickle ball
- Kicking around a soccer ball
- Gentle stretching
- Hula-hooping
- Skiing
- Ice skating
- Roller blading

You can also try doing something active with a friend and turning it into a social activity (dance party, anyone?). The social aspect helps as a distraction if your eating disorder brain is running wild with thoughts about calories and changing your bod.

It's also ok to try a few different things before you find something that you actually like. It's all about experimentation y'all. There is no wrong way to move (unless it's fueled by an eating disorder, in which case it's a hard no!). It's truly about finding something that brings you joy.

3. *Tune into your intuition.*

Listening to your body is such a helpful and important skill to develop, but diet culture literally teaches us to ignore our intuition in favor of "no days off." (Utter BS.)

Diet culture and eating disorders get you away from trusting your body. Through recovery, we want to work to cultivate that sense of body trust. Practice tuning into your needs, feelings, and body sensations when deciding whether or not to move. Try asking your bod, "what, if any, movement would you like to do today?"

There will be times when your body might be asking for a walk or a run – and other times when it's asking for gentle stretching or rest. It's important to start to honor your unique needs – without judgement or a sense of "I should" do this or "I must" do this (as therapists we're pretty anti any "shoulds" or "musts" in general).

Your body is smart and it will tell you what you need, so long as you can practice tuning into it.

4. *Make a vision of a more positive relationship with movement.*

It can also be helpful to create your own vision of what a more positive relationship with movement could look like for you. Because it's *really* hard to work towards any goal if you don't clearly define what that goal is.

If you are struggling, think of someone in your life who embodies this for an example.

My vision of a healthier relationship to movement:

_____

_____

_____

_____

_____

_____

_____

Let's be real here: you can TOTALLY transform your relationship with movement. Compulsive exercise was one of the most exhausting and difficult things that we ever went through, but being on the other side of it is so damn freeing.

At the end of your life, will you truly look back and fondly reminisce on the time that you spent chained to the treadmill? No. You'll be reflecting on silly memories made, adventures you had, and your relationships. You have a life to live – one that is so much bigger than a "six pack" or the size of your thighs.

Journaling Prompts

1. List out any of your current exercise rules.
2. When thinking about taking some time off from exercise (weeks/months or longer) what fears come up for you?
3. What could you say back to those fears? Write out new mantras/coping statements.
4. How can you start to challenge some of your current exercise rules?
5. Who can help to support you in doing so?
6. What was your relationship with movement like as a little kid?
7. If someone waived a magic wand and your body would never change, what kind of movement would you do (if any)?

References

Bacon, L. (2010). *Health At Every Size: The Surprising Truth About Your Weight.* BenBella Books.

Chastain, R. (n.d.) Recognizing and resisting diet culture. National Eating Disorders Association. www.nationaleatingdisorders.org/blog/recognizing-and-resisting-diet-culture

Gill, R. (2013, Sept. 6). Radical acceptance: What it is and how to do it. DBT Peer Connections. https://ilovedbt.wordpress.com/

Headspace (n.d.). What is mindfulness? www.headspace.com/mindfulness

McCall, P. (2018, Dec. 19). 8 Reasons to take a rest day. American Council on Exercise. www.acefitness.org/education-and-resources/lifestyle/blog/7176/8-reasons-to-take-a-rest-day/

National Eating Disorders Association (n.d.) Compulsive exercise. www.nationaleatingdisorders.org/learn/general-information/compulsive-exercise

15 Intuitive Eating

Intuitive eating can be an amazing long-term goal if you are on the anti-diet journey. It is the gold standard of eating in a way that honors our appetites and our bodies. It is the Spiderman to your eating disorder's Green Lantern. So just what is this intuitive eating jam all about anyway?

The concept of intuitive eating was introduced in 1995 by dietitians Evelyn Tribole and Elyse Resch. In their book, *Intuitive Eating: A Revolutionary Program that Works*, Tribole and Resch took a radical stance: We do not fail diets. Diets fail us. They argued that dieting is a form of shorter-term starvation that is ultimately destined to fail. Throughout the book, Tribole and Resch reasoned that dieting is not an issue of will-power, but rather an issue of fighting biology.

This idea – the idea that when we diet we are warring against our own hormonal and chemical responses – makes a TON of sense. After all, as human beings, we are programmed to keep ourselves alive. Eating is an important facet of that staying alive. When we restrict our food intake, our brains basically receive the signal "HELP! WE ARE IN A FAMINE! FIND FOOD NOW!" This signal is an evolutionary throwback to the days when we were evolving as a species, and food was scarce. So, with this in mind, the bingeing response makes a hell of a lot of sense, eh? When we restrict, our brains revert back to the famine days. They send us the signals to find food as soon as possible. We can usually fight this signal for a little while, but after some long-term restriction, the brain usually takes over. Enter: a binge.

We have found viewing bingeing in this light to be super helpful. Why? Because it *destigmatizes* it. Most people tend to feel shameful after engaging in a binge. It is psychologically distressing as hell to feel as though you are out of control around food. For many, bingeing is quickly intern-ally translated as failing.

Reframing bingeing as a survival mechanism is helpful in combating this shame. You are not "lazy" for bingeing. You are not someone who lacks willpower. We are all humans who are just trying to survive. Bingeing is a survival mechanism. It is a chemical and hormonal response to perceived starvation. Bingeing is our bodies' way of trying hard as hell to keep us alive. In that sense, *thank goodness for bingeing.*

Once we destigmatize bingeing and diet "failure," we take a step towards taking the power back from restriction-misery. See ya shame. Later hater.

Colleen

I want you to know that I fully thought intuitive eating was a joke when I first heard about it. Hunger cues? What are those? Satiety? Don't know her. It took me years of work to be able to come around to the idea of intuitive eating as a valid way to engage with food. Do you know what has been the most healing element of my intuitive eating journey? My son. My son is three months old as I write this. He poops his pants and can barely lift his head up. But he can tell me when he is hungry (lawd above can he tell me). And he can stop eating when he is full. He came into the world with these skills. (Basically the ONLY skills he has!) He was born with this wisdom. So was I. So were you. We have it in us, we just have to find a way to re-learn this!

Whew – now back to Tribole and Resch:

Tribole and Resch argued that, in light of all the evidence that diets lead to weight gain, bingeing, and inevitable feelings of failure, we should discard dieting and instead embrace intuitive eating. Intuitive eating, they said, is nurturing and listening to your body. It is a rejection of starvation and compensation, in favor of getting back in touch with your body's hunger and fullness cues and food preferences (Tribole & Resch, 1995).

Intuitive eating is going back to basics – the way we were all born to eat. Babies cry for food, have some milk and stop when they are full. Bing bang boom. Easy peasy breezy intuitive eaters those babes. When given access to all different types of food, toddlers will (generally) naturally eat a balance of different food groups. We are born with the ability to intuitively eat. It is diet culture havoc that steals this ability from us. As we age and absorb the messages of toxic diet culture, we lose touch with cravings. We hear messages that we *shouldn't* be craving sugar because it is bad – so we try our best to quell this craving and eat an apple instead. The craving, when dismissed over and over, will eventually take over, and we end up eating ten cookies instead of the three we would have originally had! Over time, we forget what it even feels like to simply honor a craving and *eat the damn cupcake* when we want one!

It is probably important here to also highlight what intuitive eating is *not*. It is *not* as simple as "eat whatever you want." That's not wrong necessarily – but the conversation around intuitive eating needs to be much more nuanced than that. It is *not* an excuse to forgo eating if you just "don't feel hungry" (specifically for people recovering from an eating disorder who may not have reliable hunger cues yet). It is *not* a diet. It is *not* "eat only when you're hungry, stop exactly when you're full." It is *not* something that you can fail at (even if there are bumps and turns along the road). There's no wagon to fall off of here. It is *not* an alternative to healthy eating – it's a paradigm that allows you to shift what "healthy" means to you and nourish your body in a way that is physically, mentally, emotionally, and maybe even spiritually beneficial (and honestly, what is freaking healthier than that?)

Now, we want to highlight here that the road to intuitive eating is long and winding. It is a process, and one that tends to be non-linear in nature. You cannot simply jump from disordered eating to intuitive eating. Let's say that one more time, for the people wayyyy in the back: You CANNOT simply jump from disordered eating to intuitive eating. It is a process. You will probably have to start out with a meal plan, or a more structured eating schedule. Why? Because your hunger and satiety cues are probably wonky. But after working on following a meal plan, and eating according to what your body likely needs (versus what your eating disorder is telling you it needs) hunger and satiety cues WILL return. It is a biological inevitability. So, when that happens, moving towards intuitive eating makes sense!

Tribole and Resch outlined ten principles of intuitive eating. While we would direct you to their book for the full down-low on what these principles *really* mean, here is the quick and dirty:

Principle 1: Reject the Diet Mentality: This principle basically implores you to toss the diet books, and any ideas that you may have about pursuing intentional weight loss. Throw out the ideas about trying that next fad diet, reject the "diet starts tomorrow" thoughts, and argue against the idea that this next diet will be the one that works.

Principle 2: Honor Your Hunger: This means get in touch with your bod – listen to it, learn how to understand when you are slightly hungry, versus full-on hangry – then move to honor that hunger. Eat until you are satiated. Don't stop eating because diet culture has convinced you that you "should" be full after the recommended serving size.

Principle 3: Make Peace with Food: This means going even deeper and banning any "should" or "shouldn't" messages from your food mentality all together. "All foods fit" will become your new mantra.

Principle 4: Challenge the Food Police: This principle involves actively arguing against the aforementioned "should" and "shouldn't" rules. Do not just aim to passively ignore the food police, start talking back. Replace the "If I choose the salad over the fries I am being good," with "Feck you food police! If I want fries I will honor that craving. Salad does not make me a better person and fries do not mean I am bad."

Principle 5: Feel Your Fullness: Just like Principle 1 tells you to get in touch with and honor your hunger, this principle implores that you do the same for fullness. Begin to recognize when you are full, versus overly full, versus Thanksgiving Day full. Then work on honoring that fullness by stopping eating when you feel it.

Principle 6: Discover the Satisfaction Factor: This principle is all about getting back in touch with what you actually *want* to eat. Listen to those cravings baby! Again, you are working to actively tune out the "shoulds" and instead eat what will give you pleasure.

Principle 7: Cope with Your Emotions without Using Food: While food is fine to use for comfort, self-soothing, and even boredom, this principle involves also identifying ways to manage emotions without food. Work to discover new ways to deal with anger, or ideas to manage anxiety or sadness that do not involve food. Once you do this, you give yourself choices – you have destigmatized emotional eating, but have also discovered many ways to manage emotions. Hence you can make informed choices about when to use food to self-soothe versus all of your other cool coping tools.

Principle 8: Respect Your Body: Understand and respect the fact that your body is your body – it is the shape that it is, and trying to change it is ultimately like trying to change your shoe size. As a size 8 shoe, you *might* be able to squeeze into those size 7s for a while, but at some point the discomfort will become overwhelming – you'll get blisters, your feet may swell – at some point you're gonna have to take those damn size 7s off and respect the fact that you are a size 8. Work to do the very same for your natural weight and body shape.

Principle 9: Exercise – Feel the Difference: Here is where movement for joy enters the game! Reject the boring, militant exercise for compensation. Instead, begin to discover ways to move your body that bring you happiness and peace.

Principle 10: Honor Your Health with Gentle Nutrition: This last and final principle is somewhat tricky. Basically, it involves getting in touch with your body on a deep level – now that all foods fit, you can work to understand which foods make your body feel good, and which make it feel not so good. Then, you can take the final leap of intuitive eating – eating in the "grey area" – i.e. making food choices based on BOTH pleasure and health. Yeah – like we said – tricky stuff.

You can probably sense how tough the path to intuitive eating can be. It is *so* difficult to go from black and white eating disorder rigidity to grey area "what makes my body feel good AND what do I love?" Luckily, we know that it is doable. And the journey is worth it, because the path to intuitive eating is really the path to peace. Look at it this way – you can continue like this – warring with your set point, restricting and engaging in miserable movement, eventually bingeing, rinse-and-repeat – or you can work to say "nope; this isn't working," and then actually begin to rewire your brain and reactions to make eating more of a peaceful event in your life.

Important question you might be having: *How is intuitive eating different from mindful eating?*

Glad you asked! Mindful eating is a part of intuitive eating. However, mindful eating is mostly defined as allowing yourself to engage in the experience of eating fully – i.e. immersing yourself in the sensory experience, being deeply in touch with what your body is asking for, and nurturing yourself whilst listening to hunger and fullness cues (Bays, 2009). Intuitive eating *incorporates* mindful eating; however, there is more to it than that. Intuitive eating also involves identifying and rejecting rules. It is an active program, one that stresses both cognitive and behavioral modifications. Mindful eating is necessary but not sufficient for intuitive eating.

Whoa. You may be thinking. Intuitive eating sounds great – in la la land where the sky is pink and the earth is perfect and we use unicorns instead of cars to get around. That is definitely what we were thinking when our dietitians first mentioned intuitive eating to us. "Ha!" We thought to ourselves. "Hunger cues? WTF are hunger cues? Cravings? Um just all the sugar all the time. Oh and French fries, mashed potatoes, garlic knots… Wait what were we talking about again?"

Our skepticism was warranted – after years of restriction, bingeing, and using just about every other disordered behavior in the books, intuitive eating seemed like a fantasy. It was like learning a second language. So, we started out not being able to speak the language at all. Actually, in early eating disorder recovery, we started out not *being allowed* to speak the language. Our hunger and satiety cues were so off that a meal plan was necessary for a while.

If you are someone in early eating disorder recovery, please understand that intuitive eating might be a non-option for you, as it was for us at that time. This is *ok*. We must learn to crawl before we can walk. We view meal plans as the crawling phase. It is important – essential even – to those in eating disorder recovery to take their time in this crawling phase. When hunger and satiety cues begin to re-emerge, and the eating disorder voice is a little less loud, intuitive eating may be an option.

When we finally started to – ya know – eat consistently and lay off the behaviors, our dietitians introduced us to the concept and language of intuitive eating. "Screw that," we knee-jerk thought. "I'll never get to that point." But slowly and surely, we learned a few words of that intuitive eating language, and then used those words to learn other words. Eventually the entire language of intuitive eating started to make sense. The truth? It took *years* for us to unlearn dieting and begin listening to our bodies in this way. However, the peace and the freedom that this intuitive eating journey has brought us and our clients on is indescribable. So, the tears, yelling, two steps forward, one step back, three steps forward, six steps back, fetal positioning in the corner, standing up, and falling again – was it all worth it? And will it be worth it for you? In the immortal words of *Sex and the City*'s Mr. Big – **abso-f*ckin-lutely** (Star & Seidelman, 1998).

WARNING: You may have a pull to turn intuitive eating into another diet. This is human. You have been swimming in diet-culture water since infancy, so dieting is an inevitable urge. After all, all roads lead back to micro-managing weight and food intake in our current society. So, when you begin to engage in this mentality, your brain may pull you towards thinking things like:

> "I can't eat yet because I am not at a perfect 5 on the hunger/fullness
> scale."
> Or
> "I ate until I was Thanksgiving Day full! I did not honor my satiety
> cues. I suck!"
> Or
> "I can't have anything at this holiday party because it's not what I am
> truly craving. It's not intuitive eating if I munch on pretzels when
> I really want cheese-its."

This pull to turn intuitive eating into a structured, rule-bound way of
life is understandable. However, you MUST reject it. Intuitive eating is a
path to freedom and peace. It is a journey away from the chaos and black
and white nonsense of an eating disorder. Pulling the diet culture mentality in will only serve to dilute and eventually ruin the process. So, when
you inevitably, at some point, hear the food police pipe up, or notice that
your thinking about intuitive eating has gotten a little rigid – shut it down.
Immediately. Once you get into a practice of shutting said thoughts down,
it becomes second nature over time.

Eventually the thoughts will be little more than a whisper. The whisper
of diet culture slowwwwwwly dying. Ah. What a beautiful little sound.

Journaling Prompt

Take one step towards intuitive eating by reading and signing the contract
below. Keep this contract. Print it out. Hang it on your fridge, your mirror,
or in your closet. Read it over daily as you fearlessly trek forward in your
journey towards food and weight freedom.

Anti-Disordered Eating Constitution

We, the former disordered eaters, in order to preserve our mental health,
insure a life in color, and promote our own freedom, do ordain and estab-
lish this new way of life:

- We will no longer adhere to the idea that food and weight loss are the
  way to happiness.
- We will stop all (non-medical) food restrictions. From this day forward, EVERYTHING, from cupcakes to kale, is allowed.
- We will stop forcing ourselves to eat any foods that we truly despise, in
  the name of "health."
- We will work towards being more in tune with our hunger and
  fullness cues.
- We will work towards eating in the company of others.

- We will reject the notion that any foods are "good" or "bad." We will now declare to ourselves and others that **all foods fit**.
- We will reject the "eat to survive" mentality, and instead embrace the idea that eating can involve joy and pleasure.
- We will stop skipping meals because we are "too busy," and instead make eating as much a priority as sleeping.
- We will STOP COUNTING – calories, macros, carbs, sugars, ounces, pounds. From now on, food = energy and weight = gravitational pull towards the earth. We will shout from the rooftops that numbers are no measure of worth.
- We will reject the idea that only certain types of bodies are good bodies. We will work to promote the idea that **all bodies are good bodies**, including our own.
- We will stop working against our set points, and start nurturing each of our own unique and wonderful body sizes.
- We will treat our bodies with compassion and kindness. This means that we will no longer penalize them with restriction or punishing gym routines. Instead, we will work to move our bodies for fun, and for joy. We will honor our hunger cues, satiety cues, and cravings.
- We will no longer buy into diet advertising, for we know now that "guilt-free" and "superfood" preys on our vulnerabilities. We will fully acknowledge that food is food, and tell advertisers and media messages that suggest otherwise to piss off.

_____   _____

Signature   Date

References

Bays, J. (2009). *Mindful Eating: A Guide to Rediscovering a Healthy and Joyful Relationship with Food*. Boulder, Colorado: Shambhala Publishing.

Star, D. (Writer) & Seidelman, S. (Director). (1998, June 6). Sex and the City. [Television series episode]. In J. Raab, A. Ellis, J. Rottenberg, and E. Zuritsky (Producers), *Sex and the City*. New York: HBO.

Tribole, E. & Rusch, E. (1995). *Intuitive Eating: A Revolutionary Program That Works*. New York: St. Martin's Griffin Publishing.

16 Finding Meaning

If you're going to recover from your eating disorder it's going to be INCREDIBLY helpful to connect with a deeper sense of meaning and purpose.

For us, and for nearly all of our former clients, finding meaning outside of appearance and weight was integral to actually taking the leap to full recovery.

An analogy that we like to give is to imagine that you have a bunch of jars, and only a set number of marbles. Imagine that each jar is a different area of your life (i.e. relationships, work, and hobbies). When you have a bunch of marbles in the "obsessing about weight" jar, you may have to take some out from the "relationships" jar.

We all have a limited amount of time and energy. When you are in an eating disorder your brain is typically totally caught up with thoughts about food and weight. As you are recovering and start to get your brain space back, it's important to fill it with things that are meaningful to you.

Colleen

Meaning, for me, was the turning point in this whole recovery process. My meaning was connectedness, career, and giving back to humanity. Oh yeah, and the desire to become a mama – *heart eyes*. These things were all incredibly motivating for me. Graduate school was actually helpful in this arena. Once I got a taste of how much I could relate to and therefore help those who were struggling with eating disorders – well, it was on like donkey kong. To this day, I will proudly tell anyone that my career choice saved me. My desire to give back saved me. My yearning to connect to other humans, to use my suffering to light the way for others – this saved me. Oh and my little baby guy Ezzie – he saved me too.

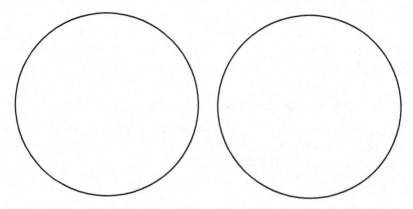

Figure 16.1 Life Percentage Exercise

An Exercise

Fill out the pie chart on the right in Figure 16.1 with what your life percentages (i.e. what you are currently spending your time doing) currently look like in categories such as, food, eating disorder, exercise, relationships, hobbies, school, work, etc. So if spending time thinking of food and weight takes up, say, 75% of your time, fill in the pie chart accordingly. If playing the violin takes up 40% of your time, fill in the chart with that. You get the deal.

Fill out the pie chart on the left with what you'd like your life percentages to look like.

What did this exercise bring up for you:

_____
_____
_____
_____

The 90-Year-Old Person Perspective

We like to talk with clients about the "90-year-old person perspective." So what the heck is it?

Well, it's sort of similar to the gravestone exercise that we introduced in the body image chapter. When thinking about what decision to make, or trying to figure out what's truly important, try asking yourself what your "90-year-old self" might think. For instance, it's unlikely that your 90-year-old self is going to be fondly reminiscing about the time you spent chained to the treadmill, the number you were on a scale, or the size of your thighs.

Nah. At the end of your life, you'll likely be reflecting on your relationships, the memories that you made, and how you pursued your passions. The 90-year-old person perspective helps you to think about the things that *truly matter*, which your eating disorder often wants to shift the focus away from.

The Top Five Regrets of the Dying

Let's chat about the five most common regrets of the dying, shall we?

We know it's a tough topic but it's another one that can be helpful when it comes to putting things into perspective.

The following are the top five regrets of the dying:

1.   *"I wish I'd had the courage to live a life true to myself, not the life others expected of me."*
2.   *"I wish I hadn't worked so hard."*
3.   *"I wish I'd had the courage to express my feelings."*
4.   *"I wish I had stayed in touch with my friends."*
5.   *"I wish that I had let myself be happier."*

(Huffpost, 2013)

Guess what isn't on that list??

> *I wish I'd had a six pack.*
> *I wish I'd eaten "clean."*
> *I wish I'd been X weight.*

Remind yourself of this when your eating disorder tries to tell you that "controling" your food, weight, and your body are SO important (spoiler: they aren't). It isn't your fault if you are focusing on things that are NOT in alignment with your true values. It's also important to talk back to your inner bully if you are having thoughts like "I'm so shallow" or "I'm so vain." This is so NOT the truth.

Focusing on food and weight is part of the symptomology for many of struggling with a disorder – NOT a character flaw or a sign of vanity.

Life Involves Pain

Anything that is meaningful or important in life also involves suffering. Some examples? Having kids ('sup labor), getting married, or following a career path. It's truly about figuring out what is *worth* suffering for.

Let's be real here: recovery takes work. Eating disorders also take work. Guess which one is actually worth it in the end?

Remember this when your eating disorder is telling you that you should throw in the towel. Recovery and finding freedom from your eating disorder will be *100% worth it*. Promise.

Searching for Meaning

Victor Frankel, author of *Man's Search for Meaning*, was a psychiatrist who survived the concentration camps in Germany (Frankl, 1984). Frankel believed that three things contributed to meaning: love, purposeful work, and courage in the face of difficult situations (Frankl, 1984).

He's quoted as saying,

> Any attempt to restore a man's inner strength in the camp had first to succeed in showing him some future goal. Nietzsche's words, 'he who has a *why* to live for can bear with almost any *how*,' could be the guiding motto for all psychotherapeutic and psychohygienic efforts regarding prisoners.

(Frankl, 1984, pp. 97–98)

When it comes to recovery it's important to explore your "why." What are your biggest motivators when it comes to working on recovery?

Jot down your answers here:

_____

_____

_____

_____

_____

It's important to note that recovery isn't simply about "wanting it enough" (or neither of us would have jobs). However, connecting to your "why" on a regular basis can be a reminder of just why the hell you are putting in the hard work. It can be awesome to post those reminders in places where you can regularly see them – for example, the lock screen of your cell phone, the wall in your room, or in your planner. The more that you can surround yourself with these ideas, the better. Especially because it is so normal for feelings of motivation to go up and down in recovery (we've both been there with ebbing motivation ourselves).

Connecting to Meaning/Purpose

So now you're thinking, ok Jennifer and Colleen – I hear ya. But how the heck can I even start to connect to a deeper sense of meaning and purpose? Well, there is no "right" way to do this, but the following are a few tips to get you started:

1. Identify something greater than yourself.

For some this might include a sense of spirituality or religion – for others it might be looking at the vastness of the ocean – or thinking about a cause that you deeply care about. It's important to start by identifying something greater than yourself, which helps to put things into perspective, and add to that sense of meaning and purpose.

What Can You Identify?

_____

_____

_____

2.   *Do things that light your soul on fire.*

Eating disorders are a joy suck. They take away the things that are meaningful to you and replace the empty spaces with a fixation on food and weight. One way to reconnect with a sense of meaning/purpose is to do things that light your soul on fire.

Have you ever been so caught up in doing something fun that you don't even notice how much time had passed? This is typically defined as a state of "flow." That's what we're aiming for here. If you don't know what that is, it's totally ok to start to explore engaging in hobbies in order to see which ones stick.

Filling your life with things that lift your spirit and take the focus away from food and weight can be so impactful to your recovery.

What lights your soul on fire?

a.

b.

c.

d.

e.

3.   *Give Back.*

Giving back to others can help you to get outside of yourself and connect with your true values. This reminds us of a quote by Aung San Suu Kyi: "If you feel helpless, help someone" (Goodreads, n.d.).

Ideas for giving back:

- Practice a random act of kindess everyday. Some ideas? Buying coffee for the person behind you in line, telling someone that you're grateful for them, or helping out your next door neighbor.
- Find a kick-ass organization to volunteer your time with.
- Show up for a friend. Ask what you can do to support them. Practice your active listening skills.

How I can give back:

_____

_____

_____

_____

Advocacy Work

Let us start out by saying that it's TOTALLY OK if you don't want to "make meaning" out of your experience of having an eating disorder. However, if ya do, advocacy work is one awesome outlet for doing so. Speaking up against diet culture and fatphobia can be a powerful part of the healing process and may help when it comes to this sense of "making meaning" out of all that you've been through.

Ideas for advocacy

- Blogging.
- Starting a podcast.
- Speaking out against diet culture that you see on Instagram.
- Joining eating disorder recovery organizations like NEDA (National Eating Disorders Association) and Project Heal.
- Leaving post it notes on diet culture things you see out and about (i.e. scales, advertisements, posters).

It's important to look at what will serve you in your recovery right now. For some people, that means talking about eating disorder-related content less and focusing on other areas of their life. For others, it means diving into advocacy work. There is no "right" answer here. You get to choose what makes the most sense for you.

Which advocacy ideas (if any) do you want to try?

_____

_____

_____

_____

The Bottom Line

We know this is a deep topic and may feel out of reach right now. When you are deep in an eating disorder it can be tough to imagine any other way of being. It can feel impossible to believe that there is anything beyond your eating disorder. But trust us when we say that connecting to a sense of purpose and meaning beyond food and your body is invaluable.

You were put here on this earth for a reason. That reason is not to spend the limited time that you have here fixated on food and weight. It's not your fault that you are struggling right now *and* there are steps that you can take to go more in the direction of the life that you want and deserve.

Jennifer

Connecting to a sense of meaning and purpose greater than myself was a really helpful element of my recovery. In tough moments, I tried to remind myself of my life goals and how I felt that they were incompatible with staying sick. I wanted to become a therapist, and it was important to me that I was in a good place to be able to do that. I also knew that I eventually wanted to have kids and that I wanted to help them to have a good relationship with food and their bodies. I also read books like *Man's Search for Meaning* which talked about how if you have a strong enough "why" you can withstand any "how." I recognized that my eating disorder had made my whole world small – consisting mainly of three things: food, weight, and exercise. I longed to have a life that was about *so much more* than my body. I knew that I couldn't get there while staying trapped in an eating disorder.

Do things that will make your future 90-year-old self proud. He/she/they is rooting for you!

Journaling Prompts

1. Imagine that you are age 90, looking back on your life. What do you imagine that you'd be focusing on at that point?
2. How can you start to shift focus to those things in the present?
3. What is your "why" when it comes to recovery? List out your biggest motivators and why they're important to you.
4. How can you start working to uncover a greater sense of meaning and purpose in your life right now?

References

Frankl, V.E. (1984). *Man's Search For Meaning: An Introduction to Logotherapy.* New York: Simon & Schuster.

Goodreads (n.d.). Aung San Suu Kyi Quotable Quotes. www.goodreads.com/author/quotes/61546.Aung_San_Suu_Kyi

Huffpost (2013, Aug. 3). The top 5 regrets of the dying. Collective Evolution. www.huffpost.com/entry/top-5-regrets-of-the-dying_n_3640593

17 Summary

Eating disorders truly are the worst. If you have read this book, we hope that by now it is clear that we have been there and we get it. Struggling with your body and your relationship with food is a constant, all-consuming battle. We can actually remember times when we sat, crumpled on the floor, our heads burrowed into our arms, and simply screamed. Screamed for how out of control we felt when it came to being able to recover. Screamed for how hopeless we felt. Screamed in anger because it wasn't supposed to be this way. It was just supposed to be a diet. It was supposed to help. It was supposed to work.

If you can relate, we see you. You are our people. We want to be sure that we acknowledge that this book is not going to be the "cure." (We wish it was! Other wishes we have had along these same lines: 1) To be the owners of "recovery magic wands," 2) To be able to jump into our clients' minds and fight their eating disorder voices by our damn selves, 3) To graduate to the status of "Recovery Fairy Godmothers"... You get the picture. We daydream a lot about healing eating disorders, ok?)

The point is, reading this book is not a quick fix, *but* it is a step. Try putting these tools and ideas to *daily* use. (The keyword here being *daily*. Eating is something that is supposed to happen daily, so healing your relationship with food must be something that you put daily work into.) Once you are challenging the thoughts, figuring out your "under the iceberg stuff," working through trauma, making friends with your emotions, and garnering support from family and friends, you will likely find that it will be harder for your eating disorder to reign over your mind with the same power.

Now remember – the realization that the disordered thoughts are getting softer may not happen at first. It may feel like a daily battle for a while, and then one day, you will wake up and think, "Hey now. I wore that outfit without experiencing any panic symptoms." Or "Whoa! I was able to stay engaged in the conversation with friends at brunch without mentally checking out to tally calories," or "OMG. I've had these cookies here for a week and haven't felt the urge to binge – I've just been eating them until I feel satiated whenever I want!"

Really sit with those realizations when you have them. As therapists, we have noticed that a lot of the work around eating disorder recovery tends to focus on how to "fix stuff." We hear a lot about what is going wrong. We talk to people a lot about how painful the process is. There can be a tendency to ignore the small wins – a tendency to ignore *what is going right!* We even noticed this for ourselves – a lot of our recovery involved focusing on how far we had to go, and very little acknowledging how far we had come. We want to encourage you to notice all the small positives. You can even write 'em down! Document the glimmers of hope along the journey in a "recovery wins" journal. Why the hell not, right?

Right now, as you are finishing up this book, you may be having thoughts along the line of:

"Well maybe other people can reach strong recovery or full recovery but not me."

or

"I'm hopeful but I've been hopeful before and then have fallen right back into the same patterns."

or

"This all sounds like so much work. It feels frustrating. I'm exhausted just thinking about it."

We want to validate all of these thoughts and emotions. All of them. It is so understandable to feel tired, hopeless, and frustrated. AND (hey-o grey area thinking) we want you to know that you CAN do this. Hold your fear. Hold that frustration. And keep.trying.anyway.

As past therapists have said to us (and as we now say to our own clients): you already know how to have a disordered relationship with food. You've already seen what happens. Why not give healing a try?

There is a whole life out there – a big, terrifying, wonderful, painful, happy, chaotic, blissful, terrible, beautiful life. Your eating disorder may say that recovered life is too uncertain, too scary. It will try to convince you that numb, black and white safety in numbers is preferable. Hear us when we say – it is not. Life in color, with all of its ups and downs, is *so* much better. *Your* life in color is out here waiting for you. Today is a great day to keep striving for it.

We'll be over here, cheering you on every step of the way.

Index

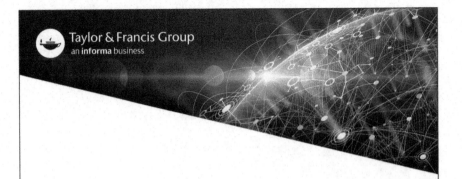